BEST O ACOUSTIC CHORD SONGBOOK

Published by
Wise Publications,
8/9 Frith Street, London W1D 3JB, England.

Exclusive Distributors:
Music Sales Limited,
Distribution Centre, Newmarket Road,
Bury St Edmunds, Suffolk, IP33 3YB, England.
Music Sales Pty Limited,
120 Rothschild Avenue, Rosebery, NSW 2018, Australia.

Order No. AM91777
ISBN 0-7119-3900-4
This book © Copyright 2005 by Wise Publications.

Music arranged & engraved by Tom Fleming.

Printed in Malta by Gutenberg Press.

WISE PUBLICATIONS
part of The Music Sales Group
London/New York/Paris/Sydney/Copenhagen/Berlin/Madrid/Tokyo

DEAD IN THE WATER David Gray 5

WHY DOES IT ALWAYS RAIN ON ME? Travis 8

THANK YOU Dido 14

MAYBE TOMORROW Stereophonics 16

SOMETHING TO TALK ABOUT Badly Drawn Boy 18

MISSING Everything But The Girl 11

LITTLE BY LITTLE Oasis 20

LOVER LOVER LOVER Leonard Cohen 22

KARMA POLICE Radiohead 24

STRANGE AND BEAUTIFUL Aqualung 26

HIGH AND DRY Jamie Cullum 28

OVER AND OVER Morcheeba 32

NORTHERN SKY Nick Drake 30

I NEED YOU The Stands 34

CANNONBALL Damien Rice 36

JESUS Velvet Underground 38

JUST THE WAY I'M FEELING Feeder 39

HOW YOU REMIND ME Nickelback 42

THE CLOSEST THING TO CRAZY Katie Melua 44

THE SAME DEEP WATER AS ME I Am Kloot 46

FIELDS OF GOLD Eva Cassidy 48

JUST LIKE A WOMAN Bob Dylan 51

THE SOUND OF SILENCE Simon & Garfunkel 54

YOU DO SOMETHING TO ME Paul Weller 56

EVERYBODY'S TALKIN' Nilsson 58

MARLENE ON THE WALL Suzanne Vega 60

THE TIME IS NOW Moloko 63

SPARKS Röyksopp 66

MR. TAMBOURINE MAN The Byrds 68

LOVE AND AFFECTION Joan Armatrading 71

FUGITIVE MOTEL Elbow 74

FALLING Nitin Sawhney 80

UGLY MAN Rickie Lee Jones 82

DON'T KNOW WHY Regina Gilberto 84

I'M ON STANDBY Grandaddy 86

LOVE AND EVIL Jean Jacques Smoothie 88

FIREFLIES Babybird 90

THE LUCKY ONE Alison Krauss & Union Station 77

WITHOUT A WORD Headway 92

SAMBA DA BENÇÃO Bebel Gilberto 94

DEAD IN THE WATER

Words & Music by David Gray

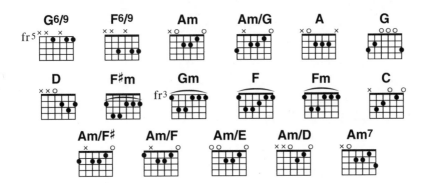

Capo first fret

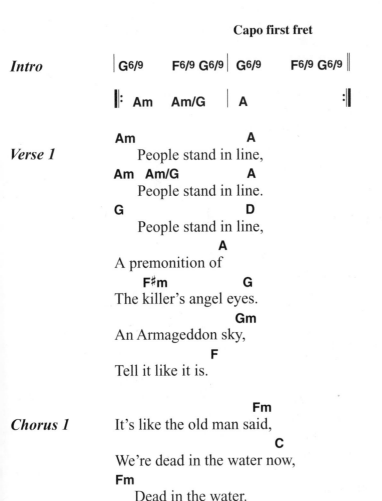

Intro

| G6/9 | F6/9 G6/9 | G6/9 | F6/9 G6/9 ||

‖: Am Am/G | A :‖

Verse 1

Am   A
People stand in line,
Am Am/G   A
People stand in line.
G   D
People stand in line,
           A
A premonition of
  F#m   G
The killer's angel eyes.
           Gm
An Armageddon sky,
       F
Tell it like it is.

Chorus 1

           Fm
It's like the old man said,
         C
We're dead in the water now,
Fm
Dead in the water.

Verse 2

Am   A
They come from miles around,
Am   A
They come from miles around.
G   D
They come from miles around,
              A
In avarice and love.
     F♯m   G
To suckle on the blood,
               Gm
Of some forgotten God.
            F
Sell it like it is.

Chorus 2

                      Fm
It's like the old man said,
                     C
We're dead in the water now,
Fm   C
We're dead in the water now.
Fm N.C.
Dead in the water.

Instrumental ‖: Am Am/G | A   :‖

Verse 3

Am   A
A simple act of faith,
Am   A
A simple act of faith.
G   D
A simple act of faith,
             A
A celebration of
     F♯m   G
The colour and the creed,
             Gm
The cancer and its seed.
            F
Crackles on the mic.

Chorus 3

            Fm
Call it what you like,

                      C
We're dead in the water now,

Fm   **C**
  We're dead in the water now,

Fm   **F**
  We're dead in the wa - ter.

Outro

| **Am** | **Am/G** | **Am/F♯** | **Am/F** |
| **Am/E** | **Am/D** | **Am⁷** | |

7

WHY DOES IT ALWAYS RAIN ON ME?

Words & Music by Fran Healy

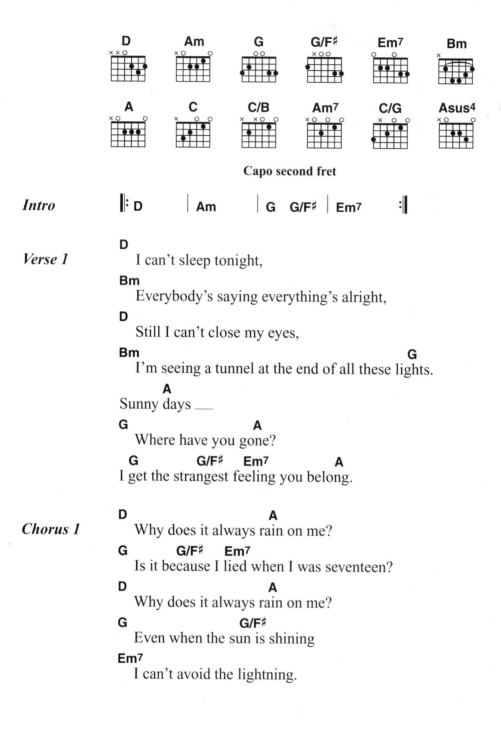

Capo second fret

Intro   ‖: D | Am | G   G/F♯ | Em7   :‖

Verse 1

D
   I can't sleep tonight,
Bm
   Everybody's saying everything's alright,
D
   Still I can't close my eyes,
Bm   G
   I'm seeing a tunnel at the end of all these lights.
        A
Sunny days ___
G   A
   Where have you gone?
G   G/F♯   Em7   A
I get the strangest feeling you belong.

Chorus 1

D   A
   Why does it always rain on me?
G   G/F♯   Em7
   Is it because I lied when I was seventeen?
D   A
   Why does it always rain on me?
G   G/F♯
   Even when the sun is shining
Em7
   I can't avoid the lightning.

Verse 2

D
  I can't stand myself,

Bm
  I'm being held up by invisible men.

D
  Still life on a shelf when

Bm
  I got my mind on something else.

G   A
  Sunny days ——

  G   A
Oh —— here have you gone?

 G   G/F♯ Em7   Asus4 A
I get the strangest feeling you belong.

Chorus 2

D   A
  Why does it always rain on me?

G G/F♯ Em7
  Is it because I lied when I was seventeen?

D   A
  Why does it always rain on me?

G   G/F♯
  Even when the sun is shining

Em7
  I can't avoid the lightning.

Middle 1

Bm   D   Bm
Oh, where did the blue skies go? — Oh,

      D   C C/B Am7
And why is it raining so?—Oh,

  C/G Asus4 A
It's so cold.

Verse 3

D
  I can't sleep tonight,

Bm
  Everybody's saying everything is alright,

D
  Still I can't close my eyes,

Bm   G
  I'm seeing a tunnel at the end of all these lights.

  A
Sunny days ——

  G   A
Oh —— where have you gone?

 G   G/F♯ Em7   Asus4 A
I get the strangest feeling you belong.

Chorus 3

D   A
Why does it always rain on me?

G   G/F♯   Em7
Is it because I lied when I was seventeen?

D   A
Why does it always rain on me?

G   G/F♯
Even when the sun is shining

Em7
I can't avoid the lightning.

Middle 2

Bm   D   Bm
Oh, where did the blue skies go? _ Oh,

                     D   C C/B Am7
And why is it raining so? _ Oh,

    C/G Asus4 A
It's so cold.

Chorus 4

D   A
Why does it always rain on me?

G   G/F♯   Em7
Is it because I lied when I was seventeen?

D   A
Why does it always rain on me?

G   G/F♯
Even when the sun is shining

Em7
I can't avoid the lightning.

D   Am   G   G/F♯ Em7
Why does it always   rain on ____ me? _____

D   Am   G G/F♯ Em7   D
Why does it always   rain on, _____ oh, on.

MISSING

Words by Tracey Thorn
Music by Ben Watt

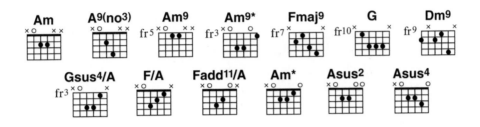

Verse 1

Am   A9(no3) Am9 A9(no3)
I step off the   train

   Am   A9(no3) Am9   A9(no3)
I'm walking down your   street again

Am   A9(no3) Am9   A9(no3)
And past your   door

  Am   A9(no3) Am9   A9(no3)
But you don't live there   any more.

   Am   A9(no3) Am9   A9(no3)
It's years since you've been   there,

Am A9(no3)   Am9   A9(no3) Am   A9(no3)
  And now you've disappeared some - where

    Am9   A9(no3) Am   A9(no3) Am9
Like outer space,   you've found some better place.

Chorus 2

A9(no3)   Am9* Fmaj9
And I miss you,

         G   Dm9
(Like the deserts miss the rain)

       Am9* Fmaj9
And I miss you   oh,

       Am9*   Dm9
(Like the deserts miss the rain).

Verse 2

Gsus4/A
        Could you be dead?

You always were two steps ahead
F/A
  Of everyone,
       Fadd11/A
We'd walk behind while you would run.
 Gsus4/A
I look up at your house

               F/A
And I can almost hear you shout

Down to me
      Fadd11/A
Where I always used to be.

Chorus 2

        Am9* Fmaj9
And I miss you,

      G   **Dm9**
(Like the deserts miss the rain)
      Am9* Fmaj9
And I miss you   oh,
      Am9*   **Dm9**
(Like the deserts miss the rain).

Verse 3

Gsus4/A
  I'm back on the train,

I ask why did I come again?
F/A   **Fadd11/A**
  Can I confess I've been hanging around your old address.
Gsus4/A
  And the years have proved

             F/A
To offer nothing sinceyou moved,

You're long gone,
Fadd11/A
  But I can't move on

Chorus 3   As Chorus 2

Verse 4
    Am*
     I step off the train
        Asus2
I'm walking down your street again
Asus4
    And past your door
       Asus2
I guess you don't live there any more.
      Am*
It's years since you've been there,
Asus4   **Am***
    And now you've disappeared some - where
         Asus2
Like outer space,   you've found some better place.

Link
       Am* **Asus2**
And I miss you, yeah.
       Am*
And I miss you.
Asus2
    You found some better place

Outro
       Am9* **Fmaj9**
‖: And I miss you,
      G   **Dm9**
(Like the deserts miss the rain)
      Am9* **Fmaj9**
And I miss you   oh,
     Am9*   **Dm9**
(Like the deserts miss the rain). :‖ *Repeat to fade*

THANK YOU

Words & Music by Dido Armstrong & Paul Herman

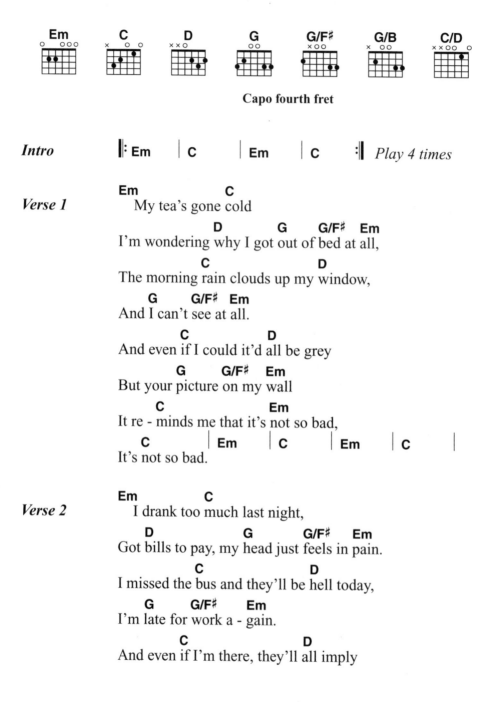

Capo fourth fret

Intro   ‖: Em | C | Em | C :‖ *Play 4 times*

Verse 1

Em   C
   My tea's gone cold
                 D   G   G/F♯ Em
I'm wondering why I got out of bed at all,
               C   D
The morning rain clouds up my window,
     G   G/F♯ Em
And I can't see at all.
            C   D
And even if I could it'd all be grey
         G   G/F♯   Em
But your picture on my wall
         C   Em
It re - minds me that it's not so bad,
      C | Em | C | Em | C |
It's not so bad.

Verse 2

Em   C
   I drank too much last night,
         D   G   G/F♯   Em
Got bills to pay, my head just feels in pain.
            C   D
I missed the bus and they'll be hell today,
     G   G/F♯   Em
I'm late for work a - gain.
          C   D
And even if I'm there, they'll all imply

     G   G/F♯   Em
That I might not last the day,

          C
And then you'll call me

       Em
And it's not so bad,

   C
It's not so bad.

Chorus 1

      G G/B   C
And I   want to thank you

     C/D   G   G/B C   C/D
For giving me the best day of my life,

     G G/B   C
And oh, just to be with you

    C/D   G/B   Am
Is having the best day of my life.

Interlude | G G/B | C C/D | G G/B | C C/D |

                | G G/B | C | G/B | Am ‖

Verse 3

G   G/B   C
   Push the door, I'm home at last

                  C/D   G
And I'm soaking through and through.

               G/B C
Then you handed me a towel,

          C/D   G
And all I see is you.

                G/B   C
And even if my house falls down now

           C/D   G/B
I wouldn't have a clue

               Am
Because you're near me.

Chorus 2   As Chorus 1

Chorus 3   As Chorus 1

MAYBE TOMORROW

Words & Music by Kelly Jones, Richard Jones & Stuart Cable

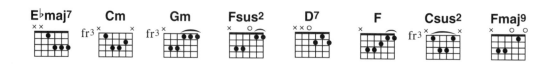

E♭maj7   Cm   Gm   Fsus2   D7   F   Csus2   Fmaj9

Intro

E♭maj7   Cm
Ooh, bap a-ooh, ooh, bap a-ooh,

Gm   Fsus2
Ooh, bap a-ooh, ooh, bap a-ooh.

Verse 1

E♭maj7
   I've been down and I'm wondering why

Cm
These little black clouds keep a-walking around

Gm
With me

Fsus2
With me.

E♭maj7
   It wastes time and I'd rather be high

Cm
Think I'll walk me outside and buy a rainbow smile

Gm
But be free,

Fsus2
They're all free.

Chorus 1

E♭maj7   Cm
   So maybe tomorrow

Gm   Fsus2
I'll find my way___ home

E♭maj7   Cm
   So maybe tomorrow

Gm   Fsus2
I'll find my way___ home.

Verse 2

E♭maj7
   I look around at a beautiful life

      Cm
I've been the upper side of down, been the inside of out

    Gm   Fsus2
But we breathe, we breathe.

E♭maj7
   I wanna breeze and an open mind

      Cm
I wanna swim in the ocean,

           Gm   Fsus2
Wanna take my time for me, all me.

Chorus 2

‖: E♭maj7   Cm
      So maybe tomorrow

        Gm   Fsus2
I'll find my way___ home

E♭maj7   Cm
  So maybe tomorrow

        Gm   Fsus2
I'll find my way___ home. :‖

Guitar solo

‖: Cm | D7 | Gm | Fmaj9 :‖

| G5 | G5 | G5 | G5 |
Ooh,   ooh,   ooh,   ooh.

Link

| E♭maj7 | Cm | Gm | Gm |

Chorus 3   As Chorus 2

Outro

| E♭maj7 | Cm | Gm | Fsus2 |

| E♭maj7 | Cm | Gm | Fsus2 |
                        Na, na, na,

| Gm | E♭maj7 | Gm | Fsus2 |
Na, na, na, na,   na, na, na, na   na, na, na, na,   na, na, na

| Gm | Gm | Gm | Fsus2 | E♭maj7 ‖
Na. Oh._____   Oh,____ oh, ah oh.

SOMETHING TO TALK ABOUT

Words & Music by Damon Gough

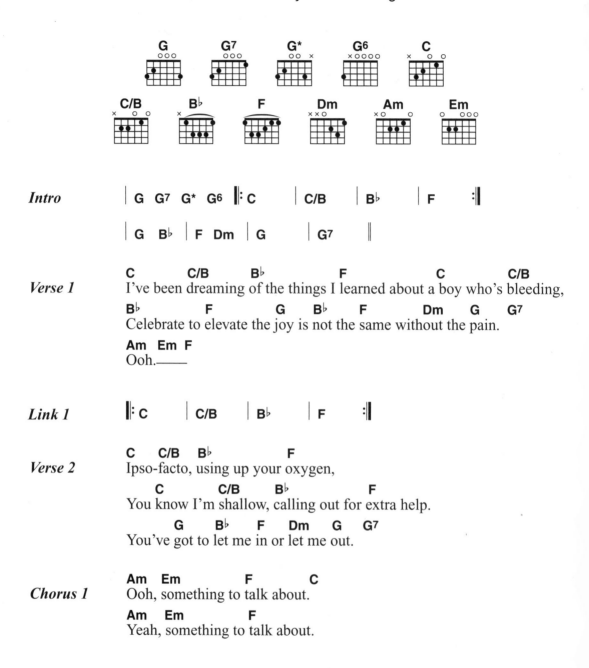

Intro | G G7 G* G6 ‖: C | C/B | Bb | F   :‖

| G Bb | F Dm | G | G7   ‖

Verse 1

C   C/B   Bb   F   C   C/B
I've been dreaming of the things I learned about a boy who's bleeding,

Bb   F   G   Bb   F   Dm   G   G7
Celebrate to elevate the joy is not the same without the pain.

Am Em F
Ooh.———

Link 1   ‖: C | C/B | Bb | F   :‖

Verse 2

C   C/B Bb   F
Ipso-facto, using up your oxygen,

        C   C/B   Bb   F
You know I'm shallow, calling out for extra help.

        G   Bb   F   Dm   G   G7
You've got to let me in or let me out.

Chorus 1

Am Em   F   C
Ooh, something to talk about.

Am Em   F
Yeah, something to talk about.

Instrumental ‖: C | C/B | B♭ | F :‖

Bridge

Am Em Dm
Ooh——

Am Em Dm
Ooh——

Am Em Dm | G G7 |
Ooh.——

Verse 3

C   C/B   B♭   F   C
I've been dreaming of the things I learned about a boy
          C/B   B♭   F
Who's leaving nothing else to chance again
          G   B♭   F   Dm   G   G7
You've got to let me in or let me out.

Chorus 2   As Chorus 1

Link 2   ‖: C | C/B | B♭ | F :‖

Outro

Am Em Dm
Ooh——

Am Em Dm
Ooh——

Am Em Dm | G | G7 G G7 G* G6 | C ‖
Ooh.——

LITTLE BY LITTLE

Words & Music by Noel Gallagher

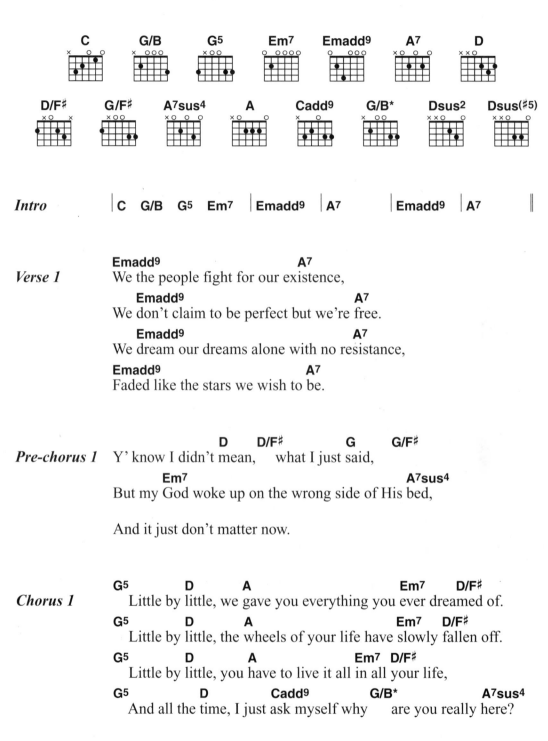

Intro |C G/B G⁵ Em⁷ |Emadd⁹ |A⁷ |Emadd⁹ |A⁷ ‖

Verse 1

Emadd⁹   A⁷
We the people fight for our existence,

   Emadd⁹   A⁷
We don't claim to be perfect but we're free.

   Emadd⁹   A⁷
We dream our dreams alone with no resistance,

Emadd⁹   A⁷
Faded like the stars we wish to be.

Pre-chorus 1

                        D   D/F♯   G   G/F♯
Y' know I didn't mean,   what I just said,

    Em⁷   A⁷sus⁴
But my God woke up on the wrong side of His bed,

And it just don't matter now.

Chorus 1

   G⁵   D   A   Em⁷   D/F♯
  Little by little, we gave you everything you ever dreamed of.

   G⁵   D   A   Em⁷   D/F♯
  Little by little, the wheels of your life have slowly fallen off.

   G⁵   D   A   Em⁷ D/F♯
  Little by little, you have to live it all in all your life,

   G⁵   D   Cadd⁹   G/B*   A⁷sus⁴
  And all the time, I just ask myself why   are you really here?

Verse 2

Emadd⁹   A⁷
True perfection has to be imperfect,

Emadd⁹   A⁷
I know that that sounds foolish but it's true.

Emadd⁹   A⁷
The day has come and now you'll have to accept,

Emadd⁹   A⁷
The life inside your head we gave to you.

Pre-chorus 2   As Pre-chorus 1

Chorus 2

G⁵   D   A   Em⁷   D/F♯
   Little by little, we gave you everything you ever dreamed of.

G⁵   D   A   Em⁷   D/F♯
   Little by little, the wheels of your life have slowly fallen off.

G⁵   D   A   Em⁷   D/F♯
   Little by little, you have to live it all in all your life,

G⁵   D   Cadd⁹   G/B*   A⁷sus⁴
   And all the time, I just ask myself why   are you really here? Hey!

Instrumental |A   G⁵ D |A |A   G⁵ D |D |D   A G⁵ |

|D   A |A   ‖

Chorus 3

G⁵   D   A   Em⁷   D/F♯
   Little by little, we gave you everything you ever dreamed of.

G⁵   D   A   Em⁷   D/F♯
   Little by little, the wheels of your life have slowly fallen off.

G⁵   D   A   Em⁷   D/F♯
   Little by little, you have to live it all in all your life,

G⁵   D   D/F♯
   And all the time, I just ask myself why you're really here.

|G⁵   D |A⁷sus⁴   Em D/F♯ |G⁵   D |

A⁷sus⁴   Em   D/F♯   G⁵   D |
   Why am I really here?

A⁷sus⁴   Em   D/F♯   G⁵   D | Cadd⁹   G⁵   ‖
   Why am I really here?

Outro   ‖: D | Dsus2 | D | Dsus2   :‖

‖: Dsus2 | G⁵ | Dsus2(♯5) | G⁵   :‖   *Repeat to fade*

21

LOVER LOVER LOVER

Words & Music by Leonard Cohen

Am   Dm   F   C

Capo seventh fret

Intro | Am | Am ‖

Verse 1

　　　　　　　　Dm
I asked my father,

　　　　　　　　　　　　　Am
I said, "Father change my name.

　　　　　　　　Dm
The one I'm using now, it's covered up

　　　　　　　　　　　　　　　　　Am
With fear and filth and cowardice and shame."

Chorus 1

　　　　　　　F　　　　　　　　　　　　　　　　　　　　　　**C**
Yes and lover, lover, lover, lover, lover, lover, lover come back to me,

　　　　　　　F　　　　　　　　　　　　　　　　　　　　　　**C**
Yes and lover, lover, lover, lover, lover, lover, lover come back to me.

Verse 2

　　　　　　　　Dm
He said, "I locked you in this body,

　　　　　　　　　　Am
I meant it as a kind of trial.

　　　　　　　　Dm
You can use it for a weapon,

　　　　　　　　　　Am
Or to make some woman smile."

Chorus 2　　　As Chorus 1

                                    Dm
Verse 3   "Then let me start again", I cried,
                                          Am
                 "Please let me start again,
                                    Dm
                 I want a face that's fair this time,
                                          Am
                 I want a spirit that is calm."

Chorus 3   As Chorus 1

                                    Dm
Verse 4   "I never turned aside," he said,
                                          Am
                 "I never walked away.
                                    Dm
                 It was you who built the temple,
                                              Am
                 It was you who covered up my face."

Chorus 4   As Chorus 1

                                    Dm
Verse 5   And may the spirit of this song,
                                          Am
                 May it rise up pure and free.
                                    Dm
                 May it be a shield for you,
                                          Am
                 A shield against the enemy.

Chorus 5   As Chorus 1

Chorus 6   As Chorus 1   *Fade out*

KARMA POLICE

Words & Music by Thom Yorke, Jonny Greenwood, Colin Greenwood, Ed O'Brien & Phil Selway

Am   Dadd9/F#   Em   G   F   Bm   D

C/E   Em7/D   C   Em7/B   F#7   E

Intro
| Am   Dadd9/F# | Em   G |

| Am   F | Em   G |

| Am   Dadd9/F# | G   Dadd9/F# C/E   Em7/D |

| Am | Bm   D ||

Verse 1

Am   Dadd9/F#   Em
  Karma   police,
  G   Am   F   Em
Arrest this man, he talks in maths.
  G   Am
He buzzes like a fridge,
  D   G   C   Em7/B Am | Bm   D |
He's like a detuned ra - di - o.

Verse 2

Am   Dadd9/F#   Em
  Karma   police,
  G   Am   F   Em
Arrest this girl, her Hitler hairdo
  G   Am
Is making me feel ill,
  D   G   C   Em7/B Am | Bm   D |
And we have crashed her par - ty.

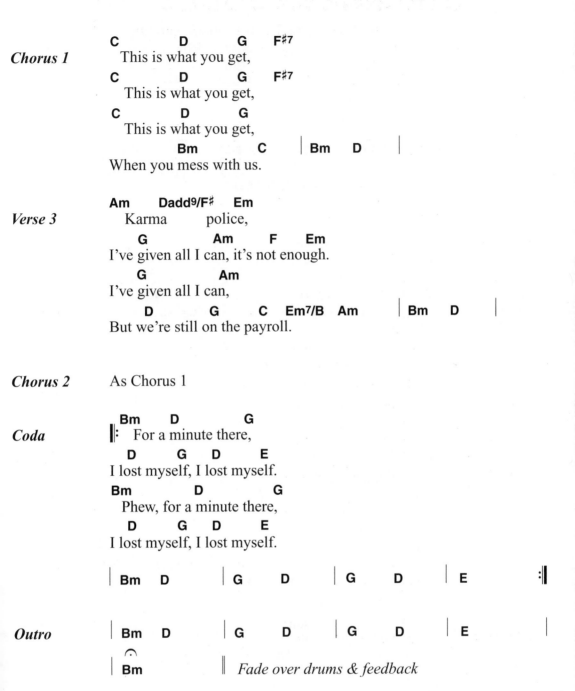

Chorus 1

C   D   G   F♯7
This is what you get,

C   D   G   F♯7
This is what you get,

C   D   G
This is what you get,

      Bm   C | Bm   D |
When you mess with us.

Verse 3

Am   Dadd9/F♯   Em
Karma   police,

   G   Am   F   Em
I've given all I can, it's not enough.

   G   Am
I've given all I can,

   D   G   C Em7/B Am | Bm   D |
But we're still on the payroll.

Chorus 2   As Chorus 1

Coda

Bm   D   G
‖: For a minute there,

   D   G   D   E
I lost myself, I lost myself.

Bm   D   G
Phew, for a minute there,

   D   G   D   E
I lost myself, I lost myself.

| Bm D | G   D | G   D | E   :‖

Outro

| Bm D | G   D | G   D | E |

| Bm ‖ *Fade over drums & feedback*

STRANGE AND BEAUTIFUL

Words & Music by Matthew Hales & Kim Oliver

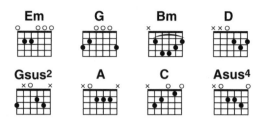

Capo third fret

Intro ¾ ‖: N.C. | N.C. :‖

‖: Em | G | Bm | D :‖

Verse 1

    Em Gsus² Bm   D   Em
I've been   watching your world from afar,
    Gsus² Bm   D   Em
I've been   trying to be where you are,
       Gsus² Bm   D   Em
And I've been   secretly falling apart,
      Gsus² Bm   D
Unseen.

Verse 2

    Em Gsus²   Bm   D
To me, you're strange and you're beautiful,
Em   Gsus² Bm   D
You'd be   so perfect with me
        Em   Gsus²
But you just can't see,
    Bm   D   Em   Gsus²   Bm D
You turn every head but you don't see me.

Chorus 1

    A   G
I'll put a spell on you,
    Em   A   G
You'll fall asleep and I'll put a spell on you,
    Em
And when I wake you,
    A   G   D
I'll be the first thing you see,
      C   G   A Asus⁴
And you'll realise that you love me.

Link

‖: Em | G | Bm | D   :‖

    Yeah...

Verse 2

Em   Gsus2   Bm   D   Em
    Sometimes, the last thing you want comes in first,

      Gsus2   Bm   D   Em
Sometimes, the first thing you want never comes.

      Gsus2   Bm   D   Em
And I know, the waiting is all you can do,

      Gsus2   Bm   D
Some - times._____

Chorus 2   As Chorus 1

Chorus 3

A   G
I'll put a spell on you,

Em   A   G
   You'll fall asleep and I'll put a spell on you,

Em
   And when I wake you,

A   G   D
I'll be the first thing you see,

     C   G   A   Asus4 A
And you'll realise that you love me,   yeah...

Outro

‖: Em | G | Bm | D   :‖   *Play 4 times*

    Yeah...

‖: Em | G | Bm | D   :‖   *Fade*

HIGH AND DRY

Words & Music by Thom Yorke, Jonny Greenwood,
Colin Greenwood & Ed O'Brien

E   Asus2   F#m11   C#m7

Tune down 1 semitone

Intro ‖: E Asus2 | Asus2 E :‖ *Play 4 times*

| E | E | E | E ‖

Verse 1

F#m11
Two jumps in a week,
   Asus2   E
I bet you think that's pretty clever don't you, boy?
F#m11
Flying on your motorcycle,
Asus2   E
Watching all the ground beneath you drop.
     F#m11
You'd kill yourself for recognition,
     Asus2   E
You'd kill yourself to never ever stop.
    F#m11
You broke another mirror,
     Asus2   E
You're turning into something you are not.

Chorus 1

        F#m11
Don't leave me high,
Asus2   E
  Don't leave me dry,
        F#m11
Don't leave me high,
Asus2
  Don't leave me dry.

Link ‖: E Asus2 | Asus2 E :‖

Verse 2

F#m11
Drying up in conversation,
Asus2   E
You will be the one who cannot talk.
F#m11
All your insides fall to pieces,
Asus2   E
   You just sit there wishing you could still make love.
F#m11
They're the ones who'll hate you,
Asus2   E
When you think you've got the world all sussed out.
F#m11
They're the ones who'll spit at you,
Asus2   E
You will be the one screaming out.

Chorus 2   As Chorus 1

Instrumental   ‖: E   Asus2 | Asus2   E   :‖

                   ‖: F#m11 | Asus2 |

                   | E | E   :‖   *Play 3 times*

                              F#m11   Asus2   E
Bridge   It's the best thing you have ever had,_____
                              F#m11   Asus2   E
                It's the best thing that you've ever had._____

Chorus 3   As Chorus 1

Instrumental 2 | E   Asus2 | Asus2   C#m7 |

                   | C#m7 Asus2 | Asus2   E |

                      E   Asus2   C#m7
Outro   ‖: Voodoodoo,   doodoodoo,
                   C#m7   Asus2   E
                   Zoodoodoo, voodoodoo. :‖ *Play 4 times ad lib.*

29

NORTHERN SKY

Words & Music by Nick Drake

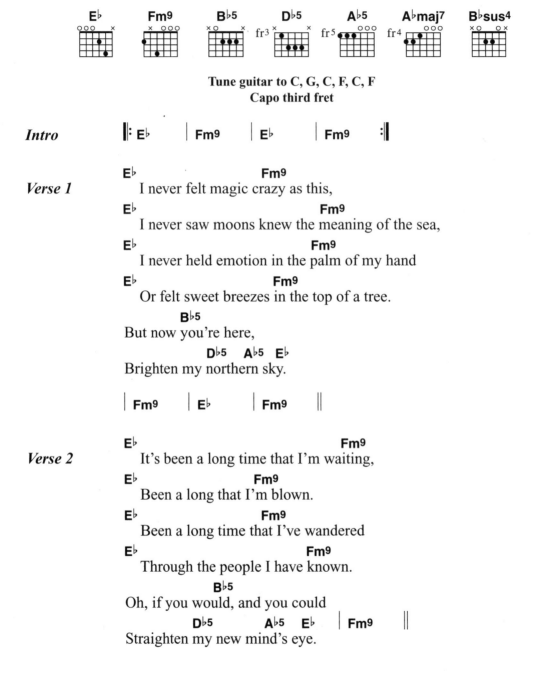

Tune guitar to C, G, C, F, C, F
Capo third fret

Intro

‖: E♭ | Fm9 | E♭ | Fm9 :‖

Verse 1

E♭   Fm9
 I never felt magic crazy as this,

E♭   Fm9
 I never saw moons knew the meaning of the sea,

E♭   Fm9
 I never held emotion in the palm of my hand

E♭   Fm9
 Or felt sweet breezes in the top of a tree.

   B♭5
But now you're here,

   D♭5 A♭5 E♭
Brighten my northern sky.

| Fm9 | E♭ | Fm9 ‖

Verse 2

E♭   Fm9
 It's been a long time that I'm waiting,

E♭   Fm9
 Been a long that I'm blown.

E♭   Fm9
 Been a long time that I've wandered

E♭   Fm9
 Through the people I have known.

    B♭5
Oh, if you would, and you could

   D♭5   A♭5 E♭ | Fm9 ‖
Straighten my new mind's eye.

Instrumental | E♭ | Fm9 | E♭ | Fm9 | E♭ Fm9 | E♭ |

‖: A♭5 A♭maj7 | E♭ :‖ *Play 3 times*

| D♭5 A♭5 | E♭ | D♭5 A♭5 | B♭sus4 | B♭sus4 ‖

Verse 3

E♭   Fm9
   Would you love me for my money?
E♭   Fm9
   Would you love me for my head?
E♭   Fm9
   Would you love me through the winter
E♭   Fm9
   Would you love me 'til I'm dead?
      B♭5
Oh, if you would and you could,
         D♭5   A♭5   E♭
Come blow your horn on   high.

| Fm9 | E♭ | Fm9 ‖

Verse 4

E♭   Fm9
   I never felt magic crazy as this,
E♭   Fm9
   I never saw moons knew the meaning of the sea,
E♭   Fm9
   I never held emotion in the palm of my hand,
E♭   Fm9
   Or felt sweet breezes in the top of a tree.
        B♭5
But now you're here,
           D♭5   A♭5   E♭
Brighten my northern ____ sky.

| Fm9 | E♭ | Fm9 | E♭ | Fm9 | E♭ Fm9 | E♭ ‖

31

OVER AND OVER

Words & Music by Paul Godfrey, Ross Godfrey & Skye Edwards

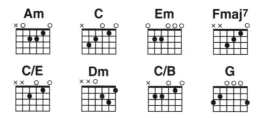

Tune down a semitone

Verse 1 | Am | Am | Am | Am   ‖

Am
Waking to these sounds again,

I wonder how I'll sleep.

Passing out is taking off into the stubborn deep,
                                C   **Em**
I'd like to meet a human who makes it all seem clear.
Am   **C**   **Em**
    To work out all these cycles and why I'm standing here,

I'm falling.

Fmaj⁷ **C/E**   **Dm**   **C**   **Am**
Chorus 1 Over and over and over and over again now,
                     C   **C/B**   **Am**   **G**   **Em**
Calling over and over and over and over again now.

Verse 2 ‖ **Am** | **Am** | **Am** | **Am** ‖

Am
Running through my life right now,

I don't regret a thing.

The things I do just make me laugh and make me wanna drink,
                       C   **Em**
I'd like to meet a mad man who makes it all seem sane.
Am   **C**   **Em**
   To work out all these troubles and what there is to gain

I'm falling.

Chorus 2   As Chorus 1

Verse 3 ‖ **Am** | **Am** | **Am** | **Am** ‖

Am
Projecting what I want is always hard to know,

But when it comes between my sights I'll let the damage show.
                       C   **Em**
I'd like to meet a space man who's got it going on,
Am   **C**   **Em**
Sailing through the stars at night until our world is gone

I'm falling.

Chorus 3   As Chorus 1

Chorus 4   As Chorus 1

I NEED YOU

Words & Music by Howard Payne

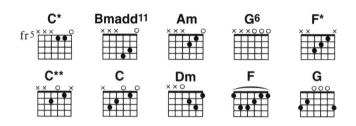

Intro $\frac{2}{4}$| C $\frac{4}{4}$| C* Bmadd11 Am   G6 $\frac{2}{4}$| F*   C** $\frac{4}{4}$|

Verse 1
           C   Dm
Out in the sunlight,
F   C
No peace I can find.
                     G   F   C
Caught up in the nights and the days we spent.

Chorus 1
            C   G
I'm down on my knees babe,
F   C
You be like I please baby.
                 Dm   F   C | C
No one needs a woman like I need you.

Verse 2
           C   Dm
I have brought something to give,
F   C
If you feel like taking it.
                   G   F   C
Come on baby sit beside me we could be alright.

Chorus 2   As Chorus 1

Instrumental

	C		Dm		F		C	
	C		G		F		C	
	C		Dm		F		C	
	C		G		F	$\frac{2}{4}$	C	$\frac{4}{4}$

| C* Bmadd11 Am G6 $\frac{2}{4}$ | F* C** $\frac{4}{4}$ |

Verse 3

C   Dm
We'll walk by the side of
F   C
This rolling river.
                       G
River wide keep rolling,
F   C
Rolling out to the sea.

Chorus 3   As Chorus 1

Outro | C* Bmadd11 Am G6 $\frac{2}{4}$ | F* C** $\frac{4}{4}$ | C ‖

35

CANNONBALL

Words & Music by Damien Rice

Am7   Fadd9   C   G/B   Dm7   F   Fsus2

Capo first fret

Intro

‖: Am7 Fadd9 | C   G/B :‖ *Play 3 times*

| Dm7 | F G/B |

Verse 1

Am7   Fadd9   C   G/B
Still a little bit of your taste in my mouth

Am7   Fadd9   C   G/B
Still a little bit of you laced with my doubt

Am7   Fadd9   C G/B
It's still a little hard to say

     Dm7 | F   G/B|
What's going on.

Verse 2

Am7   Fadd9   C   G/B
Still a little bit of your ghost, your witness,

Am7   Fadd9   C G/B
Still a little bit of your face I haven't kissed

Am7   Fadd9   C
You step a little closer each day,

  G/B   Dm7 | F   G/B|
But I can't say what's going on.

Chorus 1

C   Fsus2   G/B
Stones taught me to fly

C   Fsus2   G/B
Love taught me to lie

C   Fsus2   G/B
Life taught me to die

      Dm7
So it's not hard to fall,

      F   G/B (Am7)
When you float like a can - nonball.

Interlude   As Intro

Verse 3

Am7   Fadd9   C   G/B
   Still a little bit of your song in my ear

Am7   Fadd9   C   G/B
   There's still a little bit of your words I long to hear

Am7   Fadd9   C
   You step a little closer to me,

  G/B   Dm7 | F   G/B|
So close that I can't see what's going on.

Chorus 2

C   Fsus2   G/B
Stones taught me to fly

C   Fsus2   G/B
Love taught me to lie

C   Fsus2   G/B
Life taught me to die

       Dm7
So it's not hard to fall,

       F   G/B
When you float like a cann - on...

Chorus 3

C   Fsus2   G/B
Stones taught me to fly,

C   Fsus2   G/B
Love taught me to cry,

            C
So come on courage,

Fsus2   G/B
Teach me to be shy,

       Dm7
'Cause it's not hard to fall,

       F   G/B
And I don't wanna scare her,

    Dm7
It's not hard to fall,

       F   G/B
And I don't wanna lose,

    Dm7
It's not hard to grow,

       F   G/B   (Am7)
When you know that you just don't know.

Outro

‖: Am7 Fadd9 | C G/B | Am7 Fadd9 | C G/B |

| Am7 Fadd9 | C G/B | Dm7 | F   G/B :‖ *Play 4 times*

| Am7 |

37

JESUS

Words & Music by Lou Reed

G5 **C** **Bm** **A7** **D**
C* **Bm*** **C/G** **B*** **A***

Intro | G5 | G5 | G5 | G5 ‖

Verse 1

G5   C   G5
Jesus, help me find my proper place.
           C   G5
Jesus, help me find my proper place.
Bm   **C**
Help me in my weakness,
         A7   **C**
'Cause I'm falling out of grace.
N.C.
Jesus,

Jesus.

Link | G5 | G5 | G5 | G5 ‖

Verse 2 As Verse 1

Instrumental | G5 | G5 | G5 | G5 |

| G5 | C | G5 | G5 |

| G5 | C | G5 | G5 |

‖: D C* Bm* | C/G B* A* | G5 | G5 :‖

Verse 3 As Verse 1

JUST THE WAY I'M FEELING

Words & Music by Grant Nicholas

Bm7   D5/A   Gsus2   D5/F#   Asus4   E

Intro | Bm7 | | Bm7 | | Bm7   D5/A | D5/A   Gsus2 |

Verse 1

Bm7   D5/A   Gsus2   Bm7   D5/A   Gsus2
Love in, love out,   find the feeling.

Bm7   D5/A   Gsus2   Bm7   D5/A   Gsus2
Scream in,   scream out,   time for healing.

Bm7   D5/A   Gsus2   Bm7   D5/A   Gsus2
You feel the moments gone too soon,

Bm7   D5/A   Gsus2   Bm7   D5/A   Gsus2
You're watching clouds come over   you.

D5/F#   Gsus2
Torn in two,

Bm7   Gsus2
You close your eyes for some place new,

D5/F#   Gsus2
Torn in two.

Chorus 1

Asus4   Bm7   Gsus2
And I feel it's going down,

  D5/F#   Asus4
Ten feet below the ground,

  Bm7   Gsus2
I'm waiting for your healing hand,

  D5   Asus4
One touch could bring me round,

  Bm7   Gsus2
I feel we're going down,

  D5/F#   Asus4
Ten feet below the ground,

  Bm7   Gsus2   D5
It's just the way I'm feeling.

Link 1 ‖: Bm⁷ | Bm⁷ | D⁵/A | Gsus²   :‖

Verse 2

Bm⁷   D⁵/A   Gsus²   Bm⁷ D⁵/A Gsus²
  Glow in,   burn out, lost the feeling.
Bm⁷   D⁵/A   Gsus²   Bm⁷ D⁵/A Gsus²
  Bruise in,   you bruise out, nurse the bleeding.
D⁵/F♯   Gsus²
  Torn in two,
Bm⁷   Gsus²
  Each time we bruise.

Chorus 2

Asus⁴ Bm⁷   Gsus²
  And I feel it's going down,
    D⁵/F♯   Asus⁴
Ten feet below the ground,
    Bm⁷   Gsus²
I'm waiting for your healing hand,
    D⁵   Asus⁴
One touch could bring me round,
  Bm⁷   Gsus²
I feel we're going down,
    D⁵/F♯   Asus⁴
Ten feet below the ground,
  Bm⁷   Gsus²   D⁵
It's just the way I'm feeling
    Asus⁴ Bm⁷   Gsus²   D⁵/F♯
Yeah, yeah, it's just the way I'm feeling.

Bridge

Bm⁷   Asus⁴ Gsus²
  Two different views,
      Asus⁴ Bm⁷ Gsus²
As words confuse   and break.
Bm⁷ Asus⁴ Gsus²
  I can't get out,
      D⁵/F♯ E   D⁵/F♯ Gsus²
There's no way out   of   here,
  Asus⁴ Bm⁷ Gsus²
I can't   get clear.

Link 2 | **Bm⁷** | **Bm⁷** | **Bm⁷   D⁵/A** | **D⁵/A   Gsus²** |

           Bm⁷   **D⁵/A**   **Gsus²**   **Bm⁷**   **D⁵/A**   **Gsus²**

Verse 3   Love in,   love out,   find the feeling.

Chorus 3   As Chorus 2

           Asus⁴   **Bm⁷**   **Gsus²**   **D⁵/F♯**

Coda   Yeah, yeah, it's just the way I'm feeling,

           Asus⁴   **Bm⁷**   **Gsus²**   **D⁵/F♯**

           Yeah, yeah, it's just the way I'm feeling,

           Asus⁴   **Bm⁷**   **Gsus²**

           Yeah, yeah, it's just the way I'm feeling.

HOW YOU REMIND ME

Words & Music by Chad Kroeger,
Michael Kroeger, Ryan Peake & Ryan Vikedal

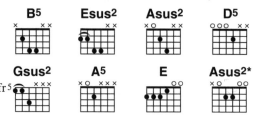

⑥ = D   Capo first fret

Verse 1

B5   Esus2
 Never made it as a wise man,
Asus2   D5
 I couldn't cut it as a poor man stealing.
B5   Esus2
Tired of living like a blind man,
Asus2   D5
 I'm sick of sight without a sense of feeling.
B5   Gsus2 Asus2
And this is how you remind me.

Chorus 1

B5 Esus2 Asus2   D5
 This is how you remind me of what I really am.
B5 Esus2 Asus2   D5
 This is how you remind me of what I really am.
B5   D5
 It's not like you to say sorry,
A5   E
 I was waiting on a different story.
B5   D5
 This time I'm mistaken,
A5   E
For handing you a heart worth breaking.
B5 N.C.   D5 N.C.
And I've been wrong, I've been down,
A5   E
 Been to the bottom of every bottle.
B5   D5
 These five words in my head,
A5   E
 Scream, "Are we having fun yet?"

cont.

B5   Esus2 A5   D5
Yet?   Yet?   Yet? No, no.

B5   Esus2 A5   D5
Yet?   Yet?   Yet? No, no.

Verse 2

B5   Esus2
It's not like you didn't know that,

Asus2   D5
I said I love you and I swear I still do.

B5   Esus2
And it must have been so bad,

Asus2   D5
'Cause living with me must have damn near killed you.

Chorus 2   As Chorus 1

Link | B5   Esus2 | Asus2 D5 |

Verse 3

B5   Esus2
Never made it as a wise man,

Asus2   D5
I couldn't cut it as a poor man stealing.

   B5   Gsus2 Asus2
And this is how you remind me,

B5   Gsus2 Asus2
This is how you remind me.

Chorus 3   As Chorus 1

Coda

B5   Esus2 A5   D5
Yet?   Yet?   Yet? No, no.

B5   Esus2 Asus2* | Asus2* |
Yet?   Yet?   Yet?

No, no.

THE CLOSEST THING TO CRAZY

Words & Music by Mike Batt

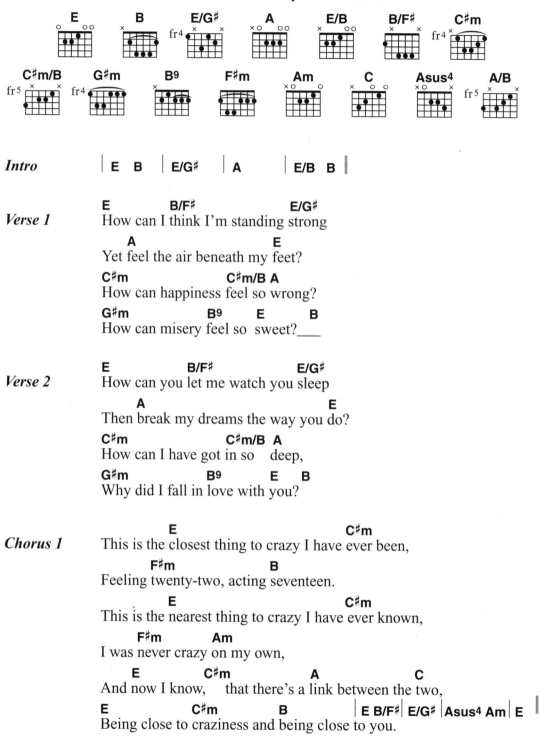

Intro | E   B | E/G♯ | A | E/B   B ||

Verse 1

　　　　　E　　　　　B/F♯　　　　　E/G♯
How can I think I'm standing strong

　　　A　　　　　　　　　　　　E
Yet feel the air beneath my feet?

C♯m　　　　　　　　　C♯m/B A
How can happiness feel so wrong?

G♯m　　　　　　B9　　　E　　　B
How can misery feel so sweet?___

Verse 2

　　　　　E　　　　　B/F♯　　　　　E/G♯
How can you let me watch you sleep

　　　A　　　　　　　　　　　　E
Then break my dreams the way you do?

C♯m　　　　　　　　　C♯m/B A
How can I have got in so   deep,

G♯m　　　　　　B9　　　E　　　B
Why did I fall in love with you?

Chorus 1

　　　　　　　　E　　　　　　　　　　　C♯m
This is the closest thing to crazy I have ever been,

　　　　F♯m　　　　　　B
Feeling twenty-two, acting seventeen.

　　　　　E　　　　　　　　　　C♯m
This is the nearest thing to crazy I have ever known,

　　F♯m　　　　Am
I was never crazy on my own,

　　　　　E　　C♯m　　　　　A　　　　　　C
And now I know,   that there's a link between the two,

E　　　　　C♯m　　　　B　　　　| E B/F♯ | E/G♯ | Asus4 Am | E ||
Being close to craziness and being close to you.

Verse 3

```
E              B/F♯              E/G♯
How can you make me fall a - part
        A                     E
Then break my fall with loving lies?
C♯m          C♯m/B  A
It's so easy to break a heart,
G♯m          B9          E    B
It's so easy to close your eyes.
```

Verse 4

```
E              B/F♯              E/G♯
How can you treat me like a child?
        A                     E
Yet like a child I yearn for you.
C♯m                C♯m/B  A
How can anyone feel so wild?
G♯m                  B9      E    B
How can anyone feel so blue?
```

Chorus 2

```
                E                        C♯m
This is the closest thing to crazy I have ever been,
        F♯m              B
Feeling twenty-two, acting seventeen.
                E                        C♯m
This is the nearest thing to crazy I have ever known,
        F♯m          Am
I was never crazy on my own,
        E        C♯m          A              C
And now I know,      that there's a link between the two,
E              C♯m          B         │E  C♯m │
Being close to craziness and being close to you,
```

Outro

```
A    B          E  C♯m
  And being close to you,
A      A/B          E
  And being close to you.
```

THE SAME DEEP WATER AS ME

Words & Music by John Bramwell,
Andrew Hargreaves & Peter Jobson

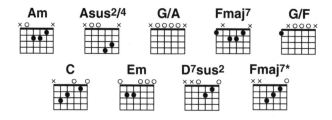

Capo second fret

Intro | Am Asus2/4 | Am G/A | Am Asus2/4 | Fmaj7 G/F ‖

Verse 1

Am   Fmaj7
Swim out to the ocean,
Am   Fmaj7
Drown your thoughts out at sea.
C   Fmaj7
And dip your hands in the water,
Em   Fmaj7
The same deep water as me.

Verse 2

Am   Fmaj7
You've been watching for cloudbursts,
Am   Fmaj7
You've been praying for rain.
C   Fmaj7
Drench your soul in the water,
Em   Fmaj7
Cleanse your heart of the stain.
Em   Fmaj7   Em
Cleanse your heart of the stain.

Instrumental ‖: D7sus2 | Fmaj7* :‖ D7sus2 | Fmaj7* | Fmaj7* ‖

Verse 3

Am   Fmaj7
The river of love,

Am   Fmaj7
Flows deep through the night.

C   Fmaj7
Rolls you in with the waves,

Em   Fmaj7
Drags you out with the tides.

Verse 4

Am   Fmaj7
Swim out to the ocean,

Am   Fmaj7
And drown our thoughts out at sea.

C   Fmaj7
And dipped your hands in the water,

Em   Fmaj7
The same deep water as me.

Em   Fmaj7   Em
The same deep water as me.

Instrumental 2 ‖: D7sus2 | Fmaj7* :‖ D7sus2 | Fmaj7* | Fmaj7 ‖

‖: Am | Fmaj7 | Am | Fmaj7 |

| C | Fmaj7 | Em | Fmaj7 :‖

| Em | Fmaj7 Em ‖

‖: D7sus2 | Fmaj7* :‖ D7sus2 | Fmaj7* | Fmaj7* ‖

‖: Am Asus2/4 | Am G/A :‖ Am ‖

47

FIELDS OF GOLD

Words & Music by Sting

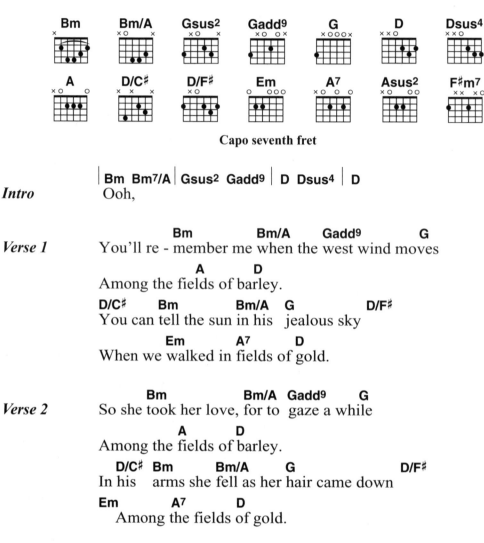

Capo seventh fret

Intro

| Bm Bm7/A | Gsus2 Gadd9 | D Dsus4 | D
Ooh,

Verse 1

     Bm   Bm/A Gadd9   G
You'll re - member me when the west wind moves
     A   D
Among the fields of barley.
D/C# Bm   Bm/A G   D/F#
You can tell the sun in his jealous sky
     Em   A7   D
When we walked in fields of gold.

Verse 2

     Bm   Bm/A Gadd9 G
So she took her love, for to gaze a while
     A   D
Among the fields of barley.
 D/C# Bm   Bm/A   G   D/F#
In his arms she fell as her hair came down
Em   A7   D
  Among the fields of gold.

Verse 3

         Bm   **Bm/A**   **Gadd⁹**   **G**
Will you stay with me?   Will you be my love

      A   **D**
Among the fields of barley?

    D/C♯   **Bm**   **Bm/A**   **G**   **D/F♯**
And you can tell the sun in his jealous sky

       Em   **A⁷**   **D**   **F♯m⁷**
When we walked in fields of gold.

Middle

  Gsus²   **A**   **D**   **D/F♯**
  I never made promises lightly,

  Gsus²   **A**   **D**   **D/F♯**
  And there have been some that I've broken,

  Gsus²   **A**   **Bm** **Bm/A**
  But I swear in the days still left,

      Gadd⁹ **Asus²** **Bm**   **Bm/A**
We will walk in fields of gold,

      Gadd⁹   **A**   **D**   **D/C♯**
We'll   walk in fields of gold.

Guitar solo

| **Bm** **Bm/A** | **Gadd⁹ G** | **G A** | **D** **D/C♯** |

| **Bm** **Bm/A** | **G** **D/F♯** | **Em A** | **D** **D/C♯** |

| **Bm** **Bm/A** | **Gadd⁹ G** | **G A** | **D** **D/C♯** |

| **Bm** **Bm/A** | **G** **D/F♯** | **Em A** | **D** **F♯m⁷** ‖

Middle 2

  Gsus²   **A**   **D**   **D/F♯**
  I never made promises lightly,

  Gsus²   **A**   **D**   **D/F♯**
  And there have been some that I've broken,

  Gsus²   **A**   **Bm** **Bm/A**
  But I swear in the days still left,

      Gadd⁹ **Asus²** **Bm**
We will walk in fields of gold,

      Gadd⁹ **A**   **D**   **D/C♯**
We'll walk in fields of gold.

Interlude

| Bm Bm/A | Gsus2 | D Dsus4 |D
Ooh._____

Verse 4

    D/C♯ Bm   Bm/A   Gadd9   G
Many   years have passed since those summer days
        A   D
Among the fields of barley.
D/C♯   Bm   Bm/A   G   D/F♯
See the children run as the sun goes down
Em   A7   D
  As you lie in fields of gold.

Verse 5

           Bm   Bm/A   Gadd9   G
You'll re - member me when the west wind moves
        A   D
Among the fields of barley.
D/C♯   Bm   Bm/A   G   D/F♯
  You can tell the sun in his jealous sky
      Em   A7   D
When we walked in fields of gold,
      Gsus2   A   Bm
When we walked in fields of gold,
Bm/A   Gadd9   A   N.C.   D
  When we walked in fields of gold.

Outro

| Bm Bm/A | Gadd9 | D Dsus4 | D   ‖
Ooh.

50

JUST LIKE A WOMAN

Words & Music by Bob Dylan

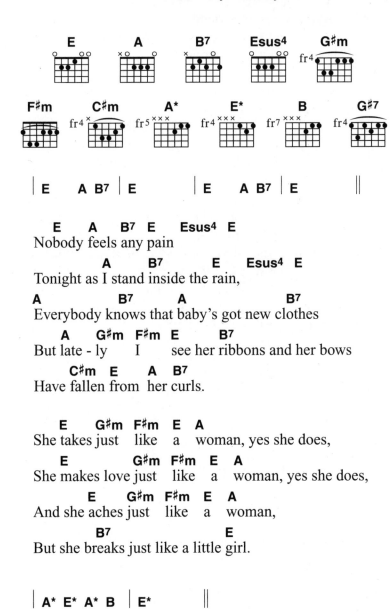

Intro | E   A B7 | E | E   A B7 | E ||

Verse 1
    E   A   B7 E   Esus4 E
Nobody feels any pain
         A   B7   E   Esus4 E
Tonight as I stand inside the rain,
A   B7   A   B7
Everybody knows that baby's got new clothes
   A G#m F#m E   B7
But late - ly   I   see her ribbons and her bows
     C#m E   A B7
Have fallen from her curls.

Chorus 1
      E   G#m F#m E A
She takes just like   a   woman, yes she does,
      E   G#m F#m E A
She makes love just like a   woman, yes she does,
        E G#m F#m E A
And she aches just like a   woman,
      B7   E
But she breaks just like a little girl.

Link | A* E* A* B | E* ||

Verse 2

        E   A   B7 E   Esus4 E
Queen Mary, she's my friend.

               A   B7   E   Esus4 E
Yes, I believe I'll go see her again.

     A   B7   A   B7
Nobody has to guess that baby can't be blessed

     A G#m F#m E   B7
Till she finally sees   that she's like all the rest

            C#m   E   A   B7
With her fog, her amphetamine   and her pearls.

Chorus 2

        E   G#m F#m E   A
She takes just like   a   woman, yes,

        E   G#m F#m E   A
She makes love just   like   a   woman, yes she does,

           E   G#m F#m E   A
And she aches just like   a   woman,

          B7   E
But she breaks just like a little girl.

Link

| A* E* A* B | E* | ||

Bridge

         G#7
It was raining from the first

And I was dying there of thirst

        E
So I came in here.

           G#7
And your   longtime curse hurts

                       A
But what's worse is this pain in here,
B7
   I can't stay in here,

Ain't it clear:

Verse 3

```
        E  A   B7  E   Esus4 E
That I  just  can't fit.
                  A      B7   E    Esus4 E
Yes, I believe it's time for us to quit.
A               B7   A            B7
When we meet again, introduced as friends,
A    G#m  F#m E  B7
Please don't let   on  that you knew me when
     C#m              G#m A B7
I was hungry and it was your    world.
```

Chorus 3

```
        E    G#m  F#m E  A
Ah you fake just  like  a  woman, yes you do,
        E      G#m  F#m E  A
You make love just  like  a  woman, yes you do,
          E   G#m  F#m E  A
Then you ache just  like  a  woman,
          B7                E
But you break just like a little girl.
```

Link

```
| A* E* A* B | E*          ||
```

Coda

```
| E    A B7 | E   Esus4 E | E    A B7 | E    Esus4 E |
| A    B7   | A   B7      | A G#m F#m E | B7          |
| C#m  E  A | B7          | E G#m F#m E | A           |
| E G#m F#m E | A         | E G#m F#m E | A           |
| B7        | A* E* A* B  | E*          ||
```

53

THE SOUND OF SILENCE

Words & Music by Paul Simon

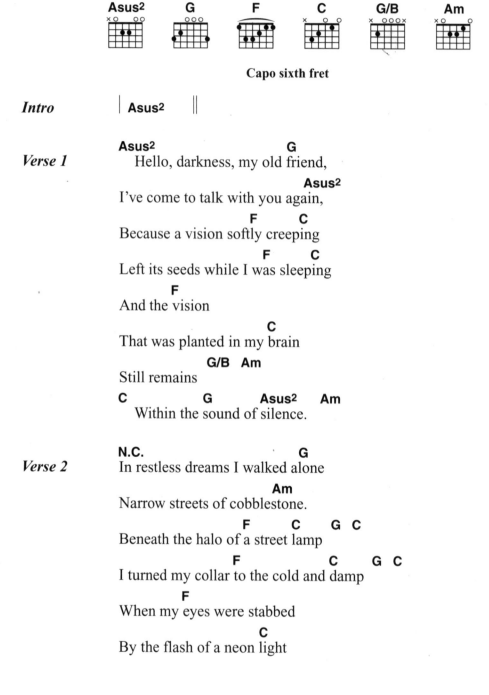

Capo sixth fret

Intro | Asus2 ||

Verse 1

Asus2   G
 Hello, darkness, my old friend,

          Asus2
I've come to talk with you again,

        F C
Because a vision softly creeping

        F C
Left its seeds while I was sleeping

     F
And the vision

        C
That was planted in my brain

       G/B Am
Still remains

C   G   Asus2 Am
 Within the sound of silence.

Verse 2

N.C.   G
In restless dreams I walked alone

         Am
Narrow streets of cobblestone.

        F C G C
Beneath the halo of a street lamp

         F   C G C
I turned my collar to the cold and damp

      F
When my eyes were stabbed

        C
By the flash of a neon light

cont.

                   G/B Am
That split the night
C   **G**   **Am**
And touched the sound of silence.

Verse 3

                      G
And in the naked light I saw
                        Am
Ten thousand people, maybe more:
             F   **C**   **G C**
People talking without speaking,
             F   **C**   **G C**
People hearing without listening,
        F   **C**
People writing songs that voices never share
          G/B Am
And no-one dare
C   **G**   **Am**
Disturb the sound of silence.

Verse 4

                  G
"Fools," said I, "You do not know
            Am
Silence like a cancer grows.
           F   **C**
Hear my words that I might teach you,
           F   **C**
Take my arms that I might reach you."
    F   **C**   **G/B Am**
But my words like silent raindrops fell,
   C   **G**   **Am**
And echoed in the wells of silence.

Verse 5

                G
And the people bowed and prayed
          Am
To the neon god they made.
            F   **C**   **G C**
And the sign flashed out its warning
         F   **C**   **G C**
In the words that it was forming,
        F
And the sign said, "The words of the prophets
      C
Are written on the subway walls
     G/B Am
And tenement halls,
   C   **G**   **Asus2**
And whispered in the sounds of silence."

55

YOU DO SOMETHING TO ME

Words & Music by Paul Weller

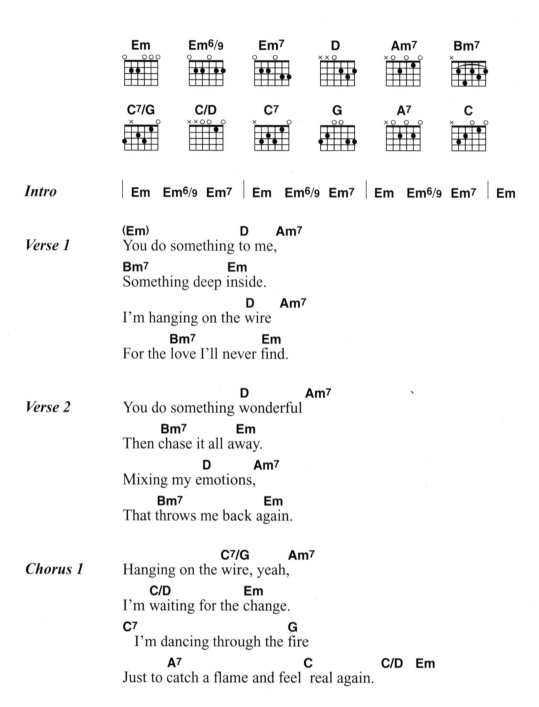

Intro
| Em Em6/9 Em7 | Em Em6/9 Em7 | Em Em6/9 Em7 | Em

Verse 1

(Em)   D   Am7
You do something to me,

Bm7   Em
Something deep inside.

D   Am7
I'm hanging on the wire

Bm7   Em
For the love I'll never find.

Verse 2

D   Am7
You do something wonderful

Bm7   Em
Then chase it all away.

D   Am7
Mixing my emotions,

Bm7   Em
That throws me back again.

Chorus 1

C7/G   Am7
Hanging on the wire, yeah,

C/D   Em
I'm waiting for the change.

C7   G
I'm dancing through the fire

A7   C   C/D Em
Just to catch a flame and feel real again.

Guitar solo   ‖: D | Am7 Bm7 | Em | Em   :‖

Chorus 2   As Chorus 1

              (Em)   **D**   **Am7**

Verse 3   You do something to me,

            Bm7   **Em**

            Somewhere deep inside.

                            D   **Am7**

            I'm hoping to get close to

             Bm7   **Em**

            A peace I cannot find.

                              C7/G   **Am7**

Chorus 3   Dancing through the fire, yeah,

            C/D   **Em**

            Just to catch a flame.

            C7   **G**

             Just to get close to,

               A7   **C7**   **C/D** **Em**

            Just close enough to tell you that:

                          D   **Am7**

            You do something to me,

            Bm7   **Em**   **Em6/9** **Em7**

             Something deep inside.

| **Em** **Em6/9** **Em7** | **Em** **Em6/9** **Em7** | **Em** **Em6/9** **Em7** | **Em** ‖

EVERYBODY'S TALKIN'

Words & Music by Fred Neil

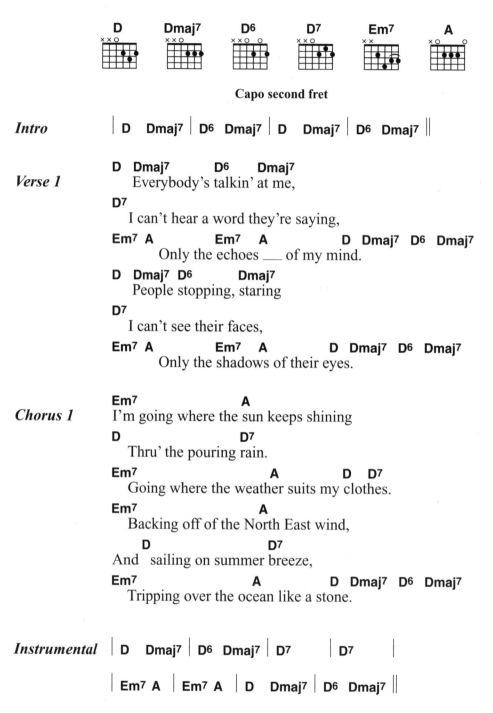

Capo second fret

Intro | D Dmaj7 | D6 Dmaj7 | D Dmaj7 | D6 Dmaj7 ||

Verse 1

D Dmaj7   D6   Dmaj7
Everybody's talkin' at me,

D7
I can't hear a word they're saying,

Em7 A   Em7   A   D Dmaj7 D6 Dmaj7
   Only the echoes __ of my mind.

D Dmaj7 D6   Dmaj7
People stopping, staring

D7
I can't see their faces,

Em7 A   Em7   A   D Dmaj7 D6 Dmaj7
   Only the shadows of their eyes.

Chorus 1

Em7   A
I'm going where the sun keeps shining

D   D7
   Thru' the pouring rain.

Em7   A   D D7
   Going where the weather suits my clothes.

Em7   A
   Backing off of the North East wind,

     D   D7
And   sailing on summer breeze,

Em7   A   D Dmaj7 D6 Dmaj7
   Tripping over the ocean like a stone.

Instrumental | D Dmaj7 | D6 Dmaj7 | D7 | D7 |

| Em7 A | Em7 A | D Dmaj7 | D6 Dmaj7 ||

Chorus 2

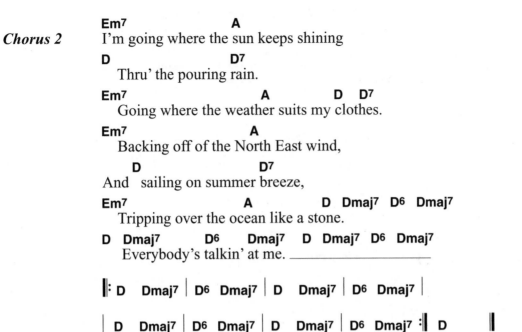

Em⁷   A
I'm going where the sun keeps shining
D   D⁷
   Thru' the pouring rain.
Em⁷   A   D   D⁷
   Going where the weather suits my clothes.
Em⁷   A
   Backing off of the North East wind,
      D   D⁷
And   sailing on summer breeze,
Em⁷   A   D Dmaj⁷ D⁶ Dmaj⁷
   Tripping over the ocean like a stone.
D   Dmaj⁷   D⁶   Dmaj⁷   D Dmaj⁷ D⁶ Dmaj⁷
   Everybody's talkin' at me. _____

‖: D   Dmaj⁷ | D⁶ Dmaj⁷ | D   Dmaj⁷ | D⁶ Dmaj⁷ |

| D   Dmaj⁷ | D⁶ Dmaj⁷ | D   Dmaj⁷ | D⁶ Dmaj⁷ :‖ D   ‖

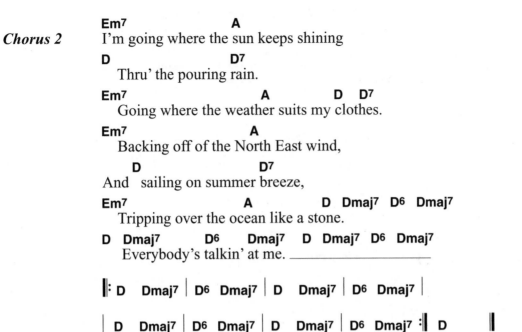

MARLENE ON THE WALL

Words & Music by Suzanne Vega

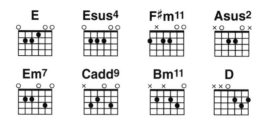

Capo second fret

Intro | E | Esus⁴ | F♯m¹¹ | Asus²   ‖

Verse 1

E
Even if I am in love with you,
   Esus⁴
All this to say, what's it to you?
  F♯m¹¹
Observe the blood, the rose tattoo,
    Asus²
Of the fingerprints on me from you.
E
  Other evidence has shown,
   Esus⁴
That you and I are still alone.
   F♯m¹¹
We skirt around the danger zone,
    Asus²
And don't talk about it later.

Chorus 1

      Em⁷   **Cadd⁹**

Marlene watches from the wall,

                         Bm¹¹

Her mocking smile says it all.

                         Cadd⁹

As she records the rise and fall

Of every soldier passing.

  Em⁷   **Cadd⁹**

But the only soldier now is me,

                         Bm¹¹

I'm fighting things I cannot see.

                    Cadd⁹

I think it's called my destiny,

That I am changing.

 D   **Cadd⁹**

Marlene on the wall.

Link 1 | **Cadd⁹** | **D** | **Cadd⁹**   ‖

             (wall.)

Verse 2

           E

Well, I walk to your house in the afternoon,

          Esus⁴

By the butcher's shop with the sawdust strewn.

F♯m¹¹

  "Don't give away the goods too soon,"

    Asus²

Is what she might have told me.

          E

And I tried so hard to resist,

          Esus⁴

When you held me in your handsome fist.

         F♯m¹¹

And reminded me of the night we kissed,

        Asus²

And of why I should I be leaving.

Chorus 2   As Chorus 1

Guitar solo | **Cadd⁹** | **D** | **Cadd⁹** | **E** | **Esus⁴** | **F♯m¹¹** |

             (wall.)

             | **Asus²** | **E** | **Esus⁴** | **F♯m¹¹** | **Asus²** ‖

Chorus 3   As Chorus 1

Link 2 | **Cadd⁹** | **D** | **Cadd⁹**   ‖
          (wall.)

Verse 3   As Verse 1

                    E
Verse 4   And I tried so hard to resist,
                        Esus⁴
          When you held me in your handsome fist,
                      F♯m¹¹
          And reminded me of the night we kissed,
                        Asus²
          And of why I should I be leaving.

          Em⁷   **Cadd⁹**
Chorus 4   Marlene watches from the wall,
                                  Bm¹¹
          Her mocking smile says it all.
                                  Cadd⁹
          As she records the rise and fall,

          Of every man who's been here.
          Em⁷   **Cadd⁹**
             But the only one here now is me,
                                  Bm¹¹
          I'm fighting things I cannot see.
                                  Cadd⁹
          I think it's called my destiny,

          That I am changing,
          D   **Cadd⁹**
          Changing, changing, changing, changing.

Chorus 5   As Chorus 1

Outro | **Cadd⁹** | **D** | **Cadd⁹** | **D** |
          (wall.)
           | **Cadd⁹** | **E**   ‖

THE TIME IS NOW

Words & Music by Mark Brydon & Roisin Murphy

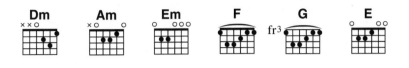

Intro
‖: Dm Am | Em Am :‖ F | G Em |

Verse 1

Dm   Am
You're my last breath,

Em   Am   Dm Am| Em Am|
You're a breath of fresh air to me.

Dm   Am
I am empty,

Em Am   Dm   Am| Em Am|
So tell me you'll care for me.

Dm   Am
You're the first thing

Em   Am   Dm   Am Em Am
And the last thing on my mind,

Dm   Am   Em Am
In your arms I feel,

F | G |
Sunshine.

Verse 2

Dm   Am
On a promise

Em Am   Dm   Am | Em Am|
A daydream yet to come.

Dm   Am   Em
Time is upon us,

Am   Dm   Am | Em Am|
Oh but the night is young.

cont.

Dm   Am   Em
Flowers blossom

Am   Dm   Am Em Am
In the winter time.

Dm   Am   Em Am
In your arms I feel

F | G |
Sunshine.

Chorus 1

Dm   Am   Em   Am
Give up your - self unto the moment,

Dm Am   Em F
The time is now.

Dm   Am   Em   Am
Give up your - self unto the moment,

F   G
Let's make this moment last.

Verse 3

Dm   Am   Em Am
You may find yourself,

Dm   Am   Em Am
Out on a limb for me,

Dm   Am   Em Am
But you accept is as

F   G
Part of your destiny.

Dm Am   Em Am
I give all I have,

Dm Am   Em Am
But it's not e - nough,

Dm Am   Em   Am
And my patience I tried

F   G
So I'm calling your bluff.

Chorus 2   As Chorus 1

Chorus 3   As Chorus 1

Middle

Dm   E
   And we gave it time,

             Am
All eyes are on the clock,

Dm   Am
   Time takes too much time,

E   Am | Dm Am
   Please make the waiting stop.

         E   Am | Dm Am
And the atmosphere is charged,

        E   Am | Dm Am
And in you I trust,

        E   Am
And I feel no fear as I

F   G
   Do as I must.

Chorus 4   As Chorus 1

Verse 4

Dm Am   Em   Am
     Tempted by fate,

Dm   Am   Em   Am
   And I won't hesi - tate,

Dm   Am   Em Am
   The time is now,

F   G
   Let's make this moment last.

          Dm   Am | Em Am |
(I'm not in love.)

Dm   Am   Em   Am | Dm Am | Em Am |
   The time is now

F   G
   Let's make this moment last.

Chorus 5

Dm   Am   Em   Am
   Give up your - self unto the moment,

Dm   Am   Em   F
   The time is now.

Dm   Am   Em   Am
   Give up your - self unto the moment,

F   G
   Let's make this moment,

Am
Last.

SPARKS

Words & Music by Svein Berge & Torbjorn Bruntland

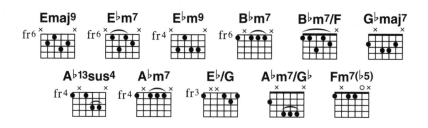

Intro

‖: Emaj⁹ | E♭m7 | Emaj⁹ | E♭m7 :‖

‖: E♭m⁹ | B♭m7 | E♭m⁹ | B♭m7 :‖

‖: E♭m⁹ | B♭m7/F | G♭maj7 | A♭13sus4 :‖

Verse 1

Emaj⁹   E♭m7
 Not much to gain or grade,
     Emaj⁹
It's those tiny little sparks
    E♭m7
Daily life that makes me
     Emaj⁹
Forget my wounded heart.
    E♭m7
It doesn't matter when,
    Emaj⁹
It may rain or it may shine.
    E♭m7
Blurry memories of us

Come back from time to time.

Instrumental

‖: E♭m⁹ | B♭m7 | E♭m⁹ | B♭m7 :‖

‖: E♭m⁹ | B♭m7/F | G♭maj7 | A♭13sus4 :‖

Verse 2   As Verse 1

Verse 3

Emaj⁹   E♭m7
   Not much to gain or grade,
                    Emaj⁹
It's those tiny little sparks
           E♭m7
Daily life that makes me
                  Emaj⁹
Forget my sulky heart.
            E♭m7
It doesn't matter when
                  Emaj⁹
It may rain or it may shine.
            E♭m7
You will always be here,

Stored inside my mind.

Bridge

A♭m7 | E♭/G | A♭m7/G♭
             Can I give you all my love?
Fm7(♭5)
Stuck some air...
A♭m7 | E♭/G | A♭m7/G♭
          Tell me what I'm dreaming of?
      Fm7(♭5)
Ooh-oh…
A♭m7 | E♭/G | A♭m7/G♭
           Maybe in a thousand years,
Fm7(♭5)
You'll be here.
A♭m7 | E♭/G | A♭m7/G♭
           Maybe within a thousand tears,
      Fm7(♭5)
Ooh-oh.

Outro   ‖: A♭m7 | E♭/G | A♭m7/G♭ | Fm7(♭5)   :‖

Repeat to fade
w/ vocal ad lib.

67

MR. TAMBOURINE MAN

Words & Music by Bob Dylan

D   G/B   A   Em

Capo third fret, sixth string tuned down a tone

Intro | D | D ||

Chorus 1

```
G/B       A                 D           G/B
Hey! Mr. Tambourine Man, play a song for me,
            D              G/B         A
I'm not sleepy and there is no place I'm going to.
G/B       A                 D           G/B
Hey! Mr. Tambourine Man, play a song for me,
            D              G/B         A        D
In the jingle jangle morning I'll come followin' you.
```

Verse 1

```
              G/B            A          D          G/B
Though I know that evenin's empire has returned into sand,
D              G/B
Vanished from my hand,
            D              G/B    Em     A
Left me blindly here to stand but still not sleeping.
    G/B       A            D            G/B
My weariness amazes me, I'm branded on my feet,
    D              G/B
I have no one to meet,
            D              G/B    Em     A
And the ancient empty street's too dead for dreaming.
```

Chorus 2   As Chorus 1

Link 1 | D | D ||

Verse 2

    G/B   A   D   G/B
Take me on a trip upon your magic swirlin' ship,

        D   G/B   D   G/B
My senses have been stripped, my hands can't feel to grip,

        D   G/B   D   Em
My toes too numb to step, wait only for my boot heels

        A
To be wanderin'.

    G/B   A   D   G/B
I'm ready to go anywhere, I'm ready for to fade

      D   G/B   D   G/B
Into my own parade, cast your dancing spell my way,

    Em   A
I promise to go under it.

Chorus 3

    G/B   A   D   G/B
Hey! Mr. Tambourine Man, play a song for me,

        D   G/B   A
I'm not sleepy and there is no place I'm going to.

G/B   A   D   G/B
Hey! Mr. Tambourine Man, play a song for me,

        D   G/B   A   D
In the jingle jangle morning I'll come followin' you.

Link 2 | D | D   ‖

Verse 3

              G/B   A
Though you might hear laughin', spinnin',

           D   G/B
Swingin' madly across the sun,

          D   G/B   D   G/B
It's not aimed at anyone, it's just escapin' on the run

          D   G/B Em   A
And but for the sky there are no fences facin'.

    G/B   A   D   G/B
And if you hear vague traces of skippin' reels of rhyme

        D   G/B   D   G/B
To your tambourine in time, it's just a ragged clown behind,

           D   G/B   D
I wouldn't pay it any mind, it's just a shadow you're

Em   A
Seein' that he's chasing.

Chorus 4   As Chorus 3

Harmonica | G/B A | D G/B | D G/B | D G/B | D G/B |
Break
              | D G/B | D Em | A | G/B A | D G/B |

              | D G/B | D G/B | D Em | A D | D   ‖

                     G/B   A   D   G/B
Verse 4   Then take me disappearin' through the smoke rings of my mind,
                         D   G/B   D   G/B
              Down the foggy ruins of time, far past the frozen leaves,
                     D   G/B   D   G/B
              The haunted, frightened trees, out to the windy beach,
                     D   G/B   Em   A
              Far from the twisted reach of crazy sorrow.
                     G/B   A   D
              Yes, to dance beneath the diamond sky with one hand waving free,
                     D   G/B   D   G/B
              Silhouetted by the sea, circled by the circus sands,
                         D   G/B   D   G/B
              With all memory and fate driven deep beneath the waves,
                         D   Em   A
              Let me forget about today until tomorrow.

Chorus 5   As Chorus 3

                                                      Fade

Coda | G/B A | D G/B | D G/B | D G/B | D G/B ‖

LOVE AND AFFECTION

Words & Music by Joan Armatrading

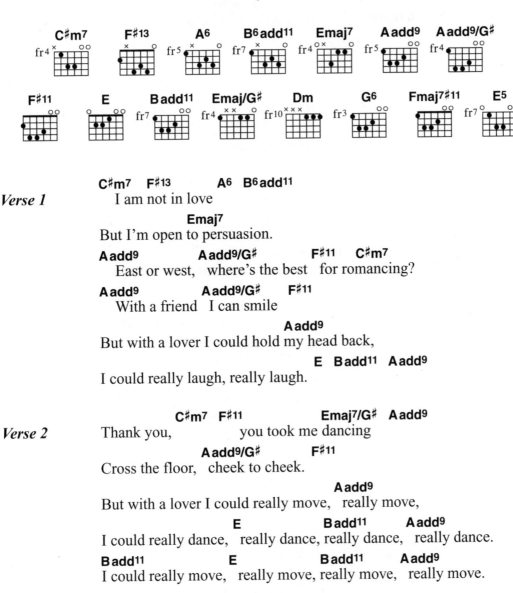

Verse 1

      C#m7 F#13   A6 B6add11
I am not in love

           Emaj7
But I'm open to persuasion.

  Aadd9   Aadd9/G#   F#11 C#m7
   East or west, where's the best for romancing?

  Aadd9   Aadd9/G#   F#11
   With a friend I can smile

                      Aadd9
But with a lover I could hold my head back,

                       E Badd11 Aadd9
I could really laugh, really laugh.

Verse 2

          C#m7 F#11   Emaj7/G# Aadd9
Thank you,   you took me dancing

           Aadd9/G#   F#11
Cross the floor, cheek to cheek.

                    Aadd9
But with a lover I could really move, really move,

             E   Badd11   Aadd9
I could really dance, really dance, really dance, really dance.

Badd11   E   Badd11   Aadd9
I could really move, really move, really move, really move.

Bridge 1

Badd11   E   Badd11 Aadd9
Now, if I can feel the sun in my eyes

                 Aadd9/G# F#11
And the rain on my face,

          C#m7 Dm(B♭bass) E   Emaj7/G# Aadd9
Why can't I feel _____   love?

Verse 3

B add¹¹   E   B add¹¹   A add⁹
I can really love, really love, really love,

        B add¹¹
Really love, really love,

E   B add¹¹   A add⁹
Love, love, love, love,   love, love, love, love.

B add¹¹   E   Emaj⁷/G♯ A add⁹   B add¹¹   E   A add⁹   B add¹¹
Now I got all _____ the friends that I want,

E   B add¹¹   A add⁹   B add¹¹
I may need more,   but I shall just stick

       E   B add¹¹   A add⁹   B add¹¹
To those things that I have got.

Bridge 2

A add⁹   B add¹¹   A add⁹ (C♯bass)
  With friends I still feel so insecure.

                 B add¹¹ (D♯bass)   A add⁹/E
Little darling, I believe you could help me a lot.

            B add¹¹ (F♯bass)   A add⁹/E
Just take my hand and lead me where you will,

         B add¹¹ (F♯bass)
No conversation, no wave goodnight.

Chorus 1

E   Emaj⁷/G♯   A add⁹   B add¹¹   E
  Just make love _____ with affection,

             Emaj⁷/G♯
Sing me another love song but

A add⁹   B add¹¹
This time with a little dedication.

      E   B add¹¹   A add⁹
Sing it, sing it,

            B add¹¹
You know that's what I like.

E   B add¹¹   A add⁹   B add¹¹
        Once more with feeling

     G⁶   F♯¹¹   Fmaj⁷♯¹¹   E⁵
Give me love, give me love, give me love,   love.

Sax solo

‖: E   B add¹¹ | A add⁹   B add¹¹ :‖ *Play 3 times*

| G⁶ | F♯¹¹ | Fmaj⁷♯¹¹ | E⁵   ‖

Chorus 2

    E   **Badd11 Aadd9**   **Badd11** **E**

Make love _____ with affection,

                        Badd11

Sing me another love song but

Aadd9   **Badd11**

This time with a little dedication.

           E   **Badd11 Aadd9**

Sing it, sing it,

                   Badd11

You know that's what I like.

E   **Badd11 Aadd9**   **Badd11 E**

Lover, oh, ooh,   once more with feeling.

                     Badd11

Sing me another love song but

Aadd9   **Badd11**

This time with a little dedication.

           E   **Badd11 Aadd9**

Sing it, sing it,

                   Badd11

You know that's what I like.

E   **Badd11 Aadd9**   **Badd11**

Lover, oh, ooh,   with affection.

E   **Badd11 Aadd9**   **Badd11**

Oh, ooh,   with a little dedication.

E   **Badd11 Aadd9**   **Badd11**

Lover, oh, ooh,   once more with feeling.

E   **Badd11 Aadd9**   **Badd11**

Oh, ooh,   you know that's what I like.

E   **Badd11 Aadd9 Badd11 E**

Lover, oh, ooh,   oh, ooh.

FUGITIVE MOTEL

Words & Music by Guy Garvey, Richard Jupp,
Peter Turner, Mark Potter & Craig Potter

E   Am   Cmaj7   Esus4/B   Bmadd11

Intro

‖: E | Am :‖

Verse 1

Cmaj7
Lost in a lullaby,
Esus4/B
Side of the road.
Cmaj7
Melts in a memory,
     Bmadd11
Slide in a solitude.
Cmaj7
Not 'til I can read by the moon,
Esus4/B
Am I going anywhere.
     Cmaj7   **Esus4/B**
Not 'til I can read by the moon.

Chorus 1

E
I blow you a kiss,
     Am
It should reach you tomorrow,
     E   **Am**
As it flies from the other side of the world.
E
From my room in my fugitive motel,
Am
Somewhere in the dust bowl,
     E   **Am**
Well, it flies from the other side of the world.

Verse 2

Cmaj7
"I'm tired," I said;

                  Esus4/B
"You always look tired," she said.

Cmaj7
"I'm admired," I said;

                  Bmadd11
"You always look tired," she said.

Cmaj7
Not 'til I can read by the moon,

Esus4/B
Am I going anywhere.

        Cmaj7   **Esus4/B**
Not 'til I can read by the moon.

Chorus 2

E
I blow you a kiss,

        Am
It should reach you tomorrow, reach you tomorrow,

      E   **Am**
It flies from the other side of the world.

E
From my room in my fugitive motel,

Am
Somewhere in the dust bowl, somewhere in the dust bowl,

      E   **Am**
It flies from the other side of the world.

Bridge

Cmaj7
The curtains stay closed,

Everyone knows,

      E
You hear through the walls in this place.

Cmaj7
Cigarette holders for every lost soul,

      E
To give up the ghost in this place.

        Cmaj7
Give me strength,

        E
Give me wings.

        Cmaj7
Give me strength,

        E
Give me wings.

                    E
Chorus 3   I blow you a kiss
                         Am
               It should reach you tomorrow, reach you tomorrow,
                    E   **Am**
               It flies from the other side of the world.
                    E
                    From my room in my fugitive motel,
               Am
               Somewhere in the dust bowl, somewhere in the dust bowl,
                    E   **Am**
               It flies from the other side of the world.
                                   Cmaj⁷ | **Bmadd¹¹**
               The other side of the world,
                                   Cmaj⁷ | **Bmadd¹¹**
               The other side of the world.
                                   Cmaj⁷ | **Cmaj⁷** | **Cmaj⁷**   ‖
               (The other side of the world.)

THE LUCKY ONE

Words & Music by Robert Castleman

A	E	F#m	Dsus2	A7	Bm	C#/E#

Capo first fret

Intro

| A | A | E | E |

| F#m | F#m | Dsus2 | Dsus2 |

| A | A | E | E |

| Dsus2 | Dsus2 | A | A |

Verse 1

      A
You're the lucky one so I've been told,

   E
As free as the wind blowing down the road.

  A7
Loved by many, hated by none,

    Dsus2
I'd say you were lucky cause I know what you've done.

     A
Not a care in the world not a worry in sight,

E
    Everything's going to be all right,

        Dsus2   **A**
'Cause you're the lucky one.

                      A
You're the lucky one always having fun,
      E
A jack of all trades a master of none.
       A7
You look at the world with a smilin' eye,
         Dsus2
And laugh at the devil as his train rolls by.
A
Give you a song and a one-night stand,
E
   You'll be looking at a happy man,
                 Dsus2   **A**
'Cause you're the lucky one.

Bridge 1

               Bm
Were you blessed? I guess,
         E
By never knowing which road you're choosing.
       Bm
To you the next best thing
              E   **C#/E#**   **F#m**
To playing and winning is playing and losing.

Verse 3

                   A
You're the lucky one, I know that now,
      E
Don't ask you why, when, where or how.
      A7
You look at the world through your smilin' eye,
        Dsus2
And laugh at the devil as his train rolls by.
A
Give you a song and a one-night stand,
E
   And you'll be looking at a happy man,
               Dsus2   **A**
'Cause you're the lucky one.

Guitar solo	A	A	E	E
	A7	A7	Dsus2	Dsus2
	A	A	E	E
	Dsus2	Dsus2	A	A

Bridge 2   As Bridge 1

Verse 4

              A
You're the lucky one I know that now,
         E
Don't ask you why, when, where or how.
          A7
No matter where you're at, that's where you'll be,
            Dsus2
You can bet your luck won't follow me.
          A
Just give you a song and a one-night stand,
E
   You'll be looking at a happy man,
                Dsus2   **A**
'Cause you're the lucky one.

Outro	A	A	E	E
	F♯m	F♯m	Dsus2	Dsus2
	A	A	E	E
	Dsus2	Dsus2	A	

FALLING

Words & Music by Nitin Sawhney & Matthew Hales

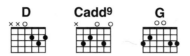

D   Cadd⁹   G

Intro | D | D | Cadd⁹ | G | D | D   ‖

Verse 1
```
D              Cadd⁹            G            D
Some day the wind will change and you will see me clearly.
D              Cadd⁹            G            D
One day these dreams of mine will bring me to my   time.
D           Cadd⁹           G                D
Some day I will become what I am meant to be coming to.
D           Cadd⁹           G                D
One day, but that's a million some days from today.
```

Verse 2
```
D              Cadd⁹          G                D
Lately the sunshine makes a different shape around me.
D            Cadd⁹      G              D
Lately my music has a different sound to show me.
     D              Cadd⁹         G                D
Oh, lately I ask questions of the world but no one's listening.
D                Cadd⁹           G              D
Tell me when I go to sleep what will the morning bring me?
```

Chorus 1
```
D                        Cadd⁹
Falling, falling, falling,
G          D
  Or am I flying?
D                        Cadd⁹
Flying, flying, flying,
G          D
  Or am I falling?
```

Chorus 2

D   Cadd⁹

D   **Cadd⁹**
Falling, falling, falling,

G   **D**
  Or am I flying?

D   **Cadd⁹**
Flying, flying, flying,

G   **D**
  Or am I falling?

       D   **Cadd⁹**
Am I fall - ing?

G   **D**
  Now am I falling?

D   **Cadd⁹**
Flying, flying, fly - ing…

G   **D**
  Am I   falling?

Outro

   D
‖: Aa hi gaye, aa hi gaye,

                      Cadd⁹
Aa hi gaye, aa hi gaye,

G   **D**
  Hum aa hi gaye.   :‖ *Play 4 times*

| **D** | **D** | **Cadd⁹** | **G** | |

      D
…or am I flying?

UGLY MAN

Words & Music by Rikki Lee Jones

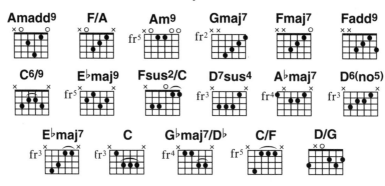

Intro $\frac{3}{4}$ ‖: **Amadd9** | **F/A** | **Am9** | **Am9** :‖

Verse 1

     Amadd9 **F/A** **Am9**
He's an ugly man,

       Amadd9   **F/A** **Am9**
He always was an ugly man.

      Amadd9 **F/A** **Am9**
He grew up to be like his father:

    Amadd9 **F/A** **Am9**
An ugly man.

      Amadd9   **F/A**   **Am9**
And he'll tell you lies,

         Amadd9   **F/A**   **Am9**
He'll look at you and tell you lies.

      Amadd9 **F/A** **Am9**
He grew up to be like his father:

    Amadd9 **F/A** **Am9**
Ug - ly in - side.

Verse 2

    Gmaj7
Hey, ugly man,

What's the plan?

  Fmaj7
If people knew, what would they do

With the ugly man?

   Gmaj7
Having fun?

cont.

But will we be here
             Fadd9   **C6/9**   **E♭maj9**
When you're done   with   me....?

Instrumental

‖: **Amadd9**	**F/A**	**Am9**	**Am9**	:‖	*Play 10 times*
Fsus2/C	**D7sus4**	**A♭maj7**	**A♭maj7**		
Fsus2/C	**D7sus4**	**D6**	**D6**		
Fsus2/C	**D7sus4**	**E♭maj7**	**C**		
G♭maj7/D♭	**G♭maj7/D♭**	**C/F**	**C/F**		
‖: **Amadd9**	**F/A**	**Am9**	**Am9**	:‖	

Verse 3

     Amadd9   **F/A**   **Am9**
Revolution,
             Amadd9   **F/A**   **Am9**
Now it's finally gonna to come,
           Amadd9 **F/A**   **Am9**
Everywhere that you're   not   looking.
Amadd9   **F/A** **Am9**
Re - vo - lu - tion,
          Amadd9   **F/A**   **Am9**
And we'll take it back.
           Amadd9   **F/A**   **Am9**
Now we take the country back,
           Amadd9 **F/A**   **Am9**
Everywhere that you're   not   looking.
Amadd9   **F/A** **Am9**
Ugly man,
Amadd9   **F/A** **Am9**
Ugly man,
Amadd9   **F/A** **Am9**
Ugly man.

Outro

‖: **Amadd9**	**F/A**	**Am9**	**Am9**	:‖	*Play 3 times*
Amadd9	**F/A**	**Am9**	**Am9** **D/G**	‖	*w/ vocal ad.lib*

83

DON'T KNOW WHY

Words & Music by Jesse Harris

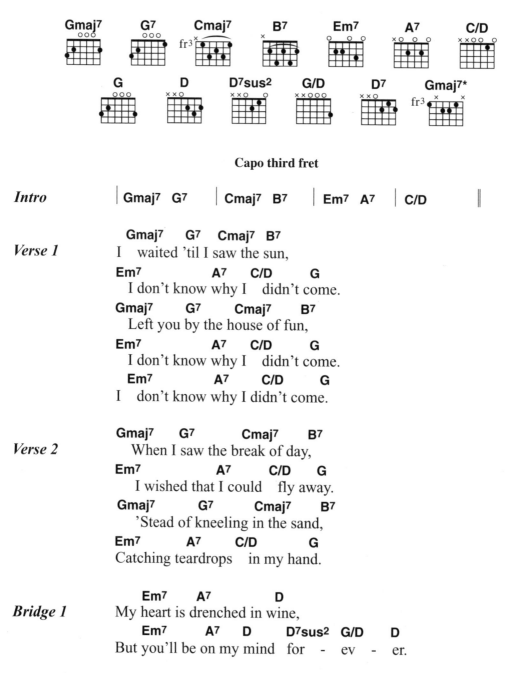

Capo third fret

Intro | Gmaj7 G7 | Cmaj7 B7 | Em7 A7 | C/D ‖

Verse 1

Gmaj7   G7 Cmaj7 B7
I   waited 'til I saw the sun,
Em7   A7   C/D   G
  I don't know why I   didn't come.
Gmaj7   G7   Cmaj7   B7
  Left you by the house of fun,
Em7   A7   C/D   G
  I don't know why I   didn't come.
  Em7   A7   C/D   G
I   don't know why I didn't come.

Verse 2

Gmaj7   G7   Cmaj7   B7
  When I saw the break of day,
Em7   A7   C/D   G
  I wished that I could   fly away.
Gmaj7   G7   Cmaj7   B7
  'Stead of kneeling in the sand,
Em7   A7   C/D   G
Catching teardrops   in my hand.

Bridge 1

   Em7   A7   D
My heart is drenched in wine,
   Em7   A7   D   D7sus2 G/D   D
But you'll be on my mind for -   ev -   er.

Verse 3

Gmaj7   G7   Cmaj7   B7
   Out across the endless sea,

Em7   A7   C/D   G
   I would die in ecstasy.

Gmaj7   G7   Cmaj7   B7
   But I'll be a bag of bones,

Em7   A7   C/D   G
Driving down the road alone.

Bridge 2   As Bridge 1

Instrumental | Gmaj7 G7 | Cmaj7 B7 | Em7 A7 | C/D |

               | Gmaj7 G7 | Cmaj7 B7 | Em7 A7 | C/D   ‖

Verse 4

Gmaj7   G7   Cmaj7   B7
   Something has to make you run,

Em7   A7   C/D   G
   I don't know why I didn't come.

Gmaj7   G7   Cmaj7   B7
   I feel as empty as a drum,

Em7   A7   C/D   G
   I don't know why I didn't come.

  Em7   A7   C/D   G
I don't know why I didn't come,

   Em7   A7   C/D   Gmaj7*
I don't know why I didn't come.

I'M ON STANDBY

Words & Music by Jason Lytle

C   Am   F   G   Dm   G7

Intro | C | C | C | C   ‖

Verse 1

C
I'm rolling down a well worn road,
     Am
I'm wondering if I'll ever know.
      F
If I'll be better than I was before,
          G   N.C.
When I surface through the service door.

Chorus 1

C   Am
I'm, I'm on standby,
          Dm   F
Out of order, sort of unaligned,
             G
Power down for redesign.
       C   Am
Bye-bye, I'm on standby,
             Dm   F
According to the work order that you signed,
                 G | G | G7   ‖
I'll be down for some time.
G7   (C)
   I'll be down for some time.

Instrumental | C | C | Am | Am |
                    (time.)
                    | Dm | F | G | G   ‖

Verse 2

        C
I got good at saying, "I gotta go,"

          Am
Number one at saying, "I don't know."

        F
But from the stories that I heard,

      G   **N.C.**
You humans require more words.

Chorus 2   As Chorus 1

Outro   ‖: C | C | Am | Am |

                 | Dm | F | G | G   :‖ *Repeat to fade*

LOVE AND EVIL

Words & Music by John Martyn & Steve Robson

Intro   ‖: Dm | Gm/B♭ | Am⁷ | Dm :‖ *Play 4 times*

Chorus 1

Dm   Gm/B♭
We don't wanna know one thing about e - vil,
   Am⁷   Dm
We only wanna know about love.
                              Gm/B♭
We don't wanna know about e - vil,
   Am⁷   Dm
We only wanna know about love.

Chorus 2   As Chorus 1

Link 1   ‖: Dm | Gm/B♭ | Am⁷ | Dm :‖

Verse 1

Dm   Gm/B♭
Sometimes it gets so hard to listen,
Am⁷   Dm
Hard for us to use our eyes.
                         Gm/B♭
And all around the gold is glistening,
   Am⁷   Dm
Making sure it keeps us hypnotised.

Verse 2   As Verse 1

Link 2

Play 4 times

‖: Dm | Gm/B♭ | Am⁷ | Dm :‖

Sometimes it gets so hard…
[1° and 2° only]

Chorus 3   As Chorus 1

Verse 3   As Verse 1

Link 3 | Dm | Gm/B♭ | Am7 | Dm |

Sometimes it gets so hard…

| Dm | Gm/B♭ | Am7 | Dm |

We don't wanna know…

Verse 4   As Verse 1

Outro | Dm | Gm/B♭ | Am7 | Dm ‖

Fade

FIREFLIES

Words & Music by Stephen Jones

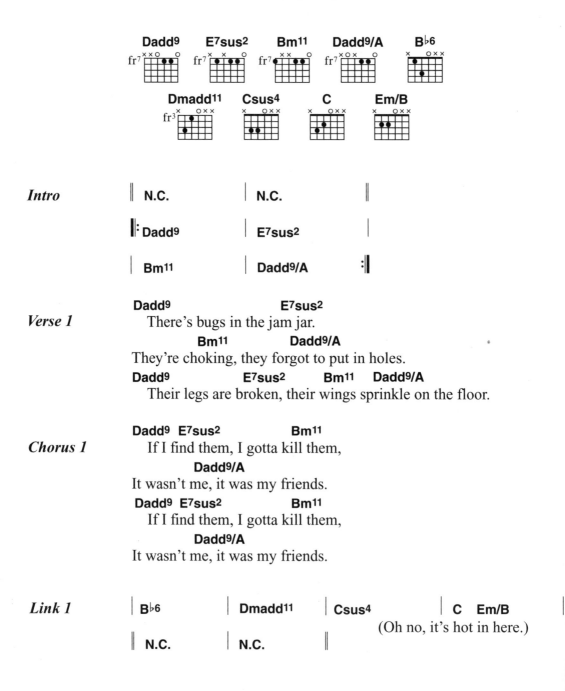

Intro

‖ N.C. | N.C. ‖

‖: Dadd9 | E7sus2 |

| Bm11 | Dadd9/A :‖

Verse 1

Dadd9   E7sus2
  There's bugs in the jam jar.
     Bm11   Dadd9/A
They're choking, they forgot to put in holes.
Dadd9   E7sus2 Bm11 Dadd9/A
  Their legs are broken, their wings sprinkle on the floor.

Chorus 1

Dadd9 E7sus2   Bm11
  If I find them, I gotta kill them,
    Dadd9/A
It wasn't me, it was my friends.
Dadd9 E7sus2   Bm11
  If I find them, I gotta kill them,
    Dadd9/A
It wasn't me, it was my friends.

Link 1

| B♭6 | Dmadd11 | Csus4 | C Em/B |
              (Oh no, it's hot in here.)

‖ N.C. | N.C. ‖

	Dadd9			**E7sus2**
Verse 2	There's bugs in the room,			

	Bm11		**Dadd9/A**
	And they're listening, I can see the fire in their tails,		

	Dadd9	**E7sus2**	**Bm11**	**Dadd9/A**
	The fireflies are hiding and listening to every single word.			

Chorus 2   As Chorus 1

Chorus 3   As Chorus 1

Link 2

B♭6	**Dmadd11**	**Csus4**	**C** **Em/B**
			(Oh no, it's hot in here.)

B♭6	**Dmadd11**	**Csus4**	**C** **Em/B**
			(Open the window, it's hot in here.)

‖ **N.C.** | **N.C.** | **Dadd9** | **E7sus2** ‖

Chorus 4   As Chorus 1

	Dadd9 **E7sus2**	**Bm11**
Chorus 5	If I find them, I gotta kill them,	

	Dadd9/A
	It wasn't me, it was my friends.

	Dadd9 **E7sus2**	**Bm11**
	If I find them, I gotta kill them,	

	Dadd9/A	**N.C.**
	It wasn't me, it was my friends.	

WITHOUT A WORD

Words & Music by David Wright

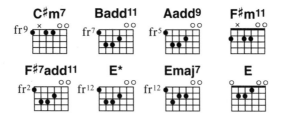

Intro $\frac{6}{8}$ | C#m7 | C#m7 | C#m7 | C#m7 |

| C#m7 | Badd11 | F#m11 | E* Emaj7 |

| C#m7 | Badd11 | F#m11 | F#7add11 |

Verse 1
C#m7   Badd11   F#m11
    If you wanted me to stay,
          E
Why'd you let me leave anyway?
C#m7   Badd11   F#m11   F#7add11
   Back and forth and round we go.
C#m7   Badd11   F#m11
   I was yours and you were mine,
     E
My intentions were pure and fine.
C#m7   Badd11   F#m11   F#7add11
 I just wanted to let you know,
     Add9   Badd11
You to know._____

Chorus 1
Add9   F#m11
   Don't you know you got nothin' to say,
Badd11   C#m7   Add9
   Don't you know you got nothin' to talk____ about
    F#m11   E
When I'm not around.

Instrumental 1 | C#m7 | Badd11 | F#m11 | E* Emaj7 |

Verse 2

C#m7   F#m11
Same old me if you fool me twice,

     E
My obsession was purely fine,

C#m7   Badd11   F#m11   F#7add11
I just wanted to let you go.

C#m7   Badd11   F#m11
And I'm still by your side,

       E
I'm just dying to be alive.

C#m7   Badd11   F#m11   F#7add11
I just wanted to let you know,

     Add9   Badd11   Add9   Badd11
You to know._____

Chorus 2   As Chorus 1

Chorus 3   As Chorus 1

Instrumental 2

Aadd9	Badd11	C#m7	C#m7	
Aadd9	Badd11	C#m7	C#m7	
F#m11	F#7add11	Aadd9	Badd11	
Badd11	Badd11	Badd11 N.C.		

Chorus 4   As Chorus 1

Chorus 5   As Chorus 1

Instrumental 3

Aadd9	Badd11	C#m7	C#m7	
Aadd9	Badd11	C#m7	C#m7	
Aadd9	Badd11	C#m7	C#m7	
Aadd9	Badd11	C#m7		

SAMBA DA BENÇÃO

Words & Music by Vinicius de Moraes & Baden Powell

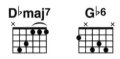

D♭maj7   G♭6

Intro | D♭maj7 | G♭6 | D♭maj7 | G♭6 |

Verse 1

     D♭maj7   G♭6
É melhor ser alegre que ser triste,
                      D♭maj7
Alegria é a melhor coisa que existe.
         G♭6
É assim como a luz   no coração,
D♭maj7   G♭6
Mas prá fazer um samba com beleza.
                D♭maj7
É preciso um bocado de tristeza,
        G♭6
É preciso um bocado de tristeza,
       D♭maj7   G♭6   D♭maj7   G♭6
Senão não se faz um samba não.

Verse 2

     D♭maj7   G♭6
Fazer samba não é contar piada,
                     D♭maj7
E quem faz samba assim não é de nada,
                    G♭6
O bom samba é uma forma de oração.

Link 1 | D♭maj7 | G♭6 | D♭maj7 | G♭6 |

Verse 3

D♭maj7   G♭6
 Porque o samba é a tristeza que balança,
            D♭maj7
E a tristeza tem sempre uma esperança.
         G♭6
E a tristeza tem sempre uma esperança,
      D♭maj7 G♭6
De um dia não ser mais triste não.
D♭maj7   G♭6
 Põe um pouco de amor numa cadência,
           D♭maj7
E vai ver que ninguém no mundo vence,.
       G♭6
A beleza que tem um samba não.

Verse 4

D♭maj7   G♭6
 Porque o samba nasceu lá na Bahia,
         D♭maj7
E se hoje ele é branco na poesia.
        G♭6
E se hoje ele é branco na poesia,
     D♭maj7 G♭6 D♭maj7 G♭6
Ele é negro demais no coração.

Verse 5

D♭maj7   G♭6
 É melhor ser alegre que ser triste,
        D♭maj7
Alegria é a melhor coisa que existe.
      G♭6 | D♭maj7 | G♭6 | D♭maj7 | G♭6 |
É assim como a luz no coração.

Verse 6

D♭maj7   G♭6
 Põe um pouco de amor numa cadência,
           D♭maj7
E vai ver que ninguém no mundo vence,
       G♭6 D♭maj7 G♭6
A beleza que tem um samba não.

Play 3 times

Instrumental ‖: D♭maj7 | G♭6 | D♭maj7 | G♭6 :‖

Verse 6   As Verse 4

Repeat to Fade

Outro ‖: D♭maj7 | G♭6 | D♭maj7 | G♭6 :‖

Relative Tuning

The guitar can be tuned with the aid of pitch pipes or dedicated electronic guitar tuners which are available through your local music dealer. If you do not have a tuning device, you can use relative tuning. Estimate the pitch of the 6th string as near as possible to E or at least a comfortable pitch (not too high, as you might break other strings in tuning up). Then, while checking the various positions on the diagram, place a finger from your left hand on the:

5th fret of the E or 6th string and **tune the open A** (or 5th string) to the note (A)

5th fret of the A or 5th string and **tune the open D** (or 4th string) to the note (D)

5th fret of the D or 4th string and **tune the open G** (or 3rd string) to the note (G)

4th fret of the G or 3rd string and **tune the open B** (or 2nd string) to the note (B)

5th fret of the B or 2nd string and **tune the open E** (or 1st string) to the note (E)

E	A	D	G	B	E
or	or	or	or	or	or
6th	5th	4th	3rd	2nd	1st

Head

Nut

1st Fret

2nd Fret

3rd Fret

4th Fret

5th Fret

Reading Chord Boxes

Chord boxes are diagrams of the guitar neck viewed head upwards, face on as illustrated. The top horizontal line is the nut, unless a higher fret number is indicated, the others are the frets.

The vertical lines are the strings, starting from E (or 6th) on the left to E (or 1st) on the right.

The black dots indicate where to place your fingers.

Strings marked with an O are played open, not fretted. Strings marked with an X should not be played.

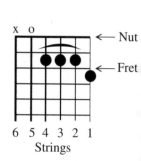

X   O
← Nut
← Fret

6 5 4 3 2 1
Strings

The curved bracket indicates a 'barre' - hold down the strings under the bracket with your first finger, using your other fingers to fret the remaining notes.

1 2 3 4 5 6 7